Past-into-Present Series

POWER

R. A. S. Hennessey

Head of the Economics Department,
The Royal Grammar School, Newcastle-upon-Tyne

B. T. BATSFORD LTD   London

First published 1972
© R. A. S. Hennessey 1972

Filmset by Keyspools Ltd, Golborne, Lancs.

Printed in Great Britain by Taylor Garnett Evans & Co. Ltd, Radlett, Herts.
for the Publishers
B. T. Batsford Ltd, 4 Fitzhardinge Street, London W1

7134 1773 0

Acknowledgment

The author and the publishers wish to thank the following for the illustrations appearing
in this book:
Aerofilms, Ltd. for figs. 15, 17; Aero Pictorial Ltd., and the British Electricity Authority
for fig. 47; The Bodleian Library for figs. 61, 62; British Broadcasting Corporation for
figs. 35 and 36; The British Museum (Natural History) for fig. 12; British Railways
for fig. 57; Maurice Broomfield and the Gas Council for fig. 31; The Burmah Oil Company
for fig. 20; Calor Gas Ltd., for fig. 56; Cambridge University Press for fig. 18; City of
Birmingham Corporation for figs. 46, 54; Department of the Environment for fig. 10;
Electrical Review for figs. 37, 38, 41, 44, 49, 51, 55; *The Electrician* for fig. 44; Electricity
Supply Board, Ireland, for fig. 42; *Flight International* for fig. 58; General Electric Co.
of America for fig. 11; *Illustrated London News* for fig. 6; London Transport Executive
for figs. 48, 53; Mansell Collection for fig. 5; Marconi Co. Ltd., for fig. 34; National
Coal Board for fig. 14; Nautical Photo Press for fig. 3; North Thames Gas Board for
figs. 25, 26; Oxford University Press (from *Voices Prophesying War* by I. F. Clarke) for
fig. 63; R. B. Parr for fig. 1; Radio Times Hulton Picture Library for figs. 2, 9, 13, 50;
Rochdale Public Library for fig. 32; Science Museum, London, for figs. 4, 33, 45; Science
Museum and Ferranti Ltd., for fig. 39; Shell Ltd., for fig. 19; South of Scotland Electricity
Board for figs. 7, 8, 52; United Kingdom Atomic Energy Authority for fig. 64; Vickers
Ltd., for fig. 59; West Midlands Gas Board for figs. 27, 28, 29, 30.

Contents

Acknowledgment   2

List of Illustrations   4

1   The Energy Problem   5

2   Sun, Wind and Water   9

3   The Fossil Fuels—(I) Coal   20

4   The Fossil Fuels—(II) Oil   36

5   Gas   45

6   Electricity   58

7   Power Applied   77

Index   94

The Illustrations

1	Halifax in 1900	6
2	Ploughing in the 1930s	9
3	Sailing Ship	10
4	Windmill pump	11
5	Ironworks at Coalbrookdale	13
6	Proposed dam for River Severn, 1924	14
7	Stonebyres generating station	16
8	Inside Stonebyres generating station	16
9	A Horsegin	17
10	Clockwork which drives Westminster Palace Clock	18
11	Early electricity pylons	19
12	Coal forest	20
13	Coal Wagon of 1916	21
14	Shakespeare colliery, Dover	23
15	Edinburgh before the Clean Air Act	25
16	Neath Abbey Patent Fuel Works	28
17	Newcastle-upon-Tyne	30
18	Oil works at Uphall	37
19	Early distillation unit of the Royal Dutch Petroleum Co.	37
20	Yenangyaung oilfield in Burma	39
21	Fuelling HMS *Iron Duke*	40
22	Modern oil refinery at Fawley	41
23	An oil tanker of 1901	42
24	One of the first road tanker lorries	42
25	Gas City: Beckton Works	46
26	Inside Beckton Gasworks	47
27	Inside Mond Gasworks, 1964	49
28	Works of the Mond Gas Co. in Staffordshire	50
29	Tipton Oil Gas Works	50
30	Changing demand for gas	51
31	Testing for natural gas	52
32	Rochdale Gasworks	55
33	Early electric lamp	59
34	Pioneer Marconi transatlantic wireless station	60
35	BBC transmitting station at Daventry	61
36	Inside Daventry	61
37	Selection of light bulbs from the 1920s	62
38	Early examples of domestic electric equipment	63
39	Electrical engineering for the power industry	64
40	Charles Merz	66
41	Electricity Advertising, 1926	68
42	Shannon hydro-electric scheme	70
43	Power lines near Nursling, Hants	71
44	Brighton Power Station, 1887	73
45	Early power plant at Victoria Embankment	74
46	Municipal power station Birmingham	74
47	Battersea Power Station	75
48	Lot's Road Power Station	78
49	Street lighting in 1937	79
50	Lighting in a Victorian night shelter	80
51	Electrically powered industry; cigarette factory, 1930	81
52	Maintenance of power lines above Peebles	82
53	Giant alternators at Greenwich	83
54	Victorian Engineering: Birmingham Waterworks at Whitacre	84
55	Gas engine	85
56	Calor gas sea terminal, Plymouth	86
57	Express train of about 1920	87
58	Blackburn flying-boat	87
59	Maxim machine gun, *c.* 1895	88
60	Protest notice against gas prices	89
61/ 62	Cartoons on the relative 'advantages' of oil and gas	90
63	'Martian' machine from *The War of the Worlds*	91
64	Nuclear power station at Dounreay	92

1 The Energy Problem

In 1894, B. H. Thwaite, an engineer, wrote: 'In England the secret of our industrial greatness and . . . the cause of our commercial supremacy may be revealed in our unrivalled facilities for the production of power'. Behind this grandiloquence lies a vital truth: that without power, men (or the states which they inhabit), can achieve virtually nothing. 'Power' is simply the 'ability to get things done', and it can refer to political power – ordering people this way or that. This book, however, deals with industrial or economic power – the power to control the natural world.

Our environment is not usually kind, but human artifice can modify it. It suffers extremes of climate which power can help us to heat or cool. Much of our lives is 'naturally' spent in darkness which power can illumine; indeed the three major power sources of modern times – gas, electricity and oil – started as lighting agents. Power also supports food-producers and brings their produce to market, and sustains the modern mass-entertainments like television and films. Power builds the great cities of our civilisation; it lights, heats and generally energizes them. This book describes how this total dependence on power came about.

Two basic essentials of civilisation, food and power, have generally been in short supply. Theologians once attributed this to the 'Fall of Man' who had been expelled from the Garden of Eden where there was total abundance. Since then, and perhaps for all time, men have had to hunt and cultivate most diligently for food, and to fashion heat and light to fight nature. Now the 'turbines continually do spin' as Malcolm Muggeridge noted of Stalin's Russia where the need to generate ever more power became an *idée fixe* of the economic planners. The same problem faces all states which seek to strengthen economies and give citizens a higher standard of living. Lenin thought his ultimate society of the future (Communism) was 'Socialism plus electricity' – a descriptive epithet. In this sense power is an artificial extension or enlargement of man in his struggle with the environment. It makes him faster and stronger – aero-engines take him into the sky; rockets to outer space. A crane makes him into a giant of strength and a bomb into a dispenser of earthquakes and holocausts. Power can intensify the good or evil generated by society – in itself it is morally neutral.

The energy shortage may be met by continuous technical development, but at a cost. The historic energy source, coal, serves to illustrate this. Burning coal makes smoke and fogs (in London 4,000 people were killed by a fog in 1952) and disfigures or corrodes buildings. Coal-mining is a dangerous occupation and its results have blighted large areas of countryside with slag heaps. One such heap killed over 100 children in a school at Aberfan in South Wales, when it collapsed in 1966. These children were further victims of the energy-god which supports our civilisation. Only since 1945 has a serious attempt been made to weigh the advantages against the disadvantages of big-scale power generation, particularly with regard to the pollution or ugliness it may cause (the process known technically as cost-benefit analysis). Power industries have always operated on the grand scale – their output is measured in millions of tons of coal or oil, millions of megawatts of electric power, or cubic feet of gas. The buildings which house generating plant are often of cyclopean proportions.

Power industries are based on fuels. One distinguishes between the *primary fuel*, for example, coal or oil, which supplies the source of the *secondary fuel*, gas or electricity, that is used in house and factory. Most energy is derived from the sun, the only exception being nuclear power – and that has only been exploited commercially since the mid-1950s. Fundamentally men are themselves 'sentient engines' – thinking machines. Our bodily energy is derived from eating, but only a tiny fraction of this is expended in nervous or mechanical energy. Much is wasted as heat: the average person gives off one kilowatt per hour (1 kWh). Our fuel is food, and this is usually animal or plant life, itself sun-nourished; plants are the basic animal fuel and they are in effect a means of converting solar energy into edible form. The most efficient energy-converting plant is sugar beet which holds two per cent of the sun's energy falling on it (in fact 0·5 per cent is a good figure for any crop). Edible animals, like rabbits or sheep, are even less efficient tappers of solar energy, since they feed on already inefficient plants.

A well-fed human is, therefore, not the most efficient of creations if considered solely as a power-generator. Until the Industrial Revolution (*c.* 1780–1840) social and economic development was held back by the low mechanical efficiency of power-supplies: beasts and men, and such other transformers of solar energy

1 Answers to the power problem: Halifax, in the West Riding of Yorkshire *circa 1900*, showing virtually all forms of primary and secondary fuel at once: coal burning mills, containing steam engines; gas lamps; electric trams; horses—and even a small boy pulling a cart. Somewhere above is the single greatest source of heat and light, the sun.

permitted by the simple reigning technology (windmills and watermills and sailing ships). Not only was the efficiency of these things low, but their total output of power was very limited and erratic.

The last two centuries could well be called the 'age of power' although one hesitates to add another time-span cliché to an already rich series. Even so, the presiding theme of all economic change (and resulting social change) of modern times has been the refinement in efficiency and vastly greater output of power producers. The symbols of these revolutionary changes are the steam engine, the electric generator, the internal-combustion engine and the atomic pile.

The American polymath Buckminster Fuller has rightly said that the secret of progress (the word is used advisedly, meaning at least material progress) is 'more with less' – more energy with less fuel, less noise, pollution and waste. The total energy consumed by modern economies is gigantic by, say, medieval standards. The power needed to move trains and cars, to light streets and drawing rooms or for that matter to send bombers on raids and rockets to the moon has grown thus:

> 1860: 1,100 million megawatt hours
> 1900: 6,100 million megawatt hours
> 1950: 21,000 million megawatt hours

Obviously most of this was in industrialised nations; for instance, in 1950 the USA consumed 62 megawatt-hours per person, Great Britain 37, but India only 2·7. Also, before the Industrial Revolution, most energy used was in a sense 'replaceable'; millstreams flowed on, horses took a rest and ploughed on. During the Industrial Revolution society began to use up irreplaceable assets in a big way: wood, coal and oil, all of which were really stored solar energy, the latter two having lain underground and untouched for aeons. Now they are being burnt up quickly. There is a danger of the rapid dissipation of limited resources, and therefore the need to do 'more with less'. Solar energy (itself not immortal, for the sun has only a normal star's life span) is the only 'perpetual' source of power: the rest is expendable fuel, and that includes nuclear power.

To do more with less it is necessary to improve mechanical efficiency. Even in 1950, two-thirds of generated energy was wasted by transmission, noise, friction, etc. Yet progress has occurred: Watt's early steam engines (c. 1785) had an efficiency of only four per cent; the efficiency-conscious Cornish engineers brought this up to ten per cent by 1830 (Cornwall had to import coal from Wales, and counted costs carefully), and a good Parsons turbine of 1910 had brought the figure up to twenty per cent. Today it could be forty per cent.

The earliest fuel used in Great Britain was probably wood; we know from archaeological remains that elsewhere in the world wood was burnt for fuel in 350,000 B.C. Very much later coal was employed, and later still, mineral oil. Here one refers to common usage – not freakish 'firsts' or exceptions. Coal and oil (the 'fossil fuels' – so called because of their origins) came to be used later because their gathering requires at least a modicum of technical sophistication, obviously far beyond the resources of primitive men. Large reserves of easily-exploitable coal lying near the surface led to the development of Britain's first coal fields in Scotland at the Firth of Forth, and in Northumberland and Durham, from the early thirteenth century. Oil, lying generally deeper, was not used widely until the nineteenth century. Besides the fossil fuels, solar energy (via the 'weather engine') has continued to be used, and often in a highly developed way, such as hydro-electricity.

The artefacts of the pre-industrial era were certainly not mean or crude. As far as we know, the great pyramids of Egypt were erected by muscle-power; as were the soaring Gothic cathedrals of the Middle Ages and the Great Wall of China. The fleets of Salamis and Trafalgar were launched by shipyards that did not know of the pneumatic riveter, any more than the Peruvian Incas, master road- and bridge-builders, knew of bulldozers and steam rollers. To achieve these things, and the more humdrum ones, men ground away for centuries in deadening toil.

But by wielding artificial energy, man has changed the face of the earth in less than two centuries. Millions of people's lives have been elevated above mere subsistence; but these people live in a power-fashioned civilisation which is utterly dependent upon generated energy for its existence.

> *Power . . .*
> *Makes slaves of men, and of the human frame*
> *A mechanised automaton*

thought Shelley in *Queen Mab*. He spoke of political power, but the point has validity also in connexion with 'energy power'.

Western man, like Dr Faust, seems willing to pay the price for this magical transformation; he seems to want to be a slave of 'powered civilisation'. This book tells how post-Renaissance man (in Britain in particular) has found and exploited these new sources of power, and what sort of a society has emerged as a result.

FURTHER READING
Desmond King-Hele, *The End of the Twentieth Century*
H. Thirring, *Energy for Man*
F. Cotterell, *Energy and Society*
Owen Ashmore, *Development of Power in Britain*
Books dealing with power and its generation obviously deal with technical concepts and terms. It is not the place of this book to explain these exhaustively; a good book which does so, however, is: H. J. P. Keighley and F. R. McKim, *The Physical World, Volume III.*

2 Sun, Wind and Water

The sun is the source of all power on earth, except nuclear power, but even the materials from which this comes are derived from our planet. The stars are so remote that the energy we receive from them is practically unusable. The sun is itself a star, with a surface temperature of 6,000°C, and it is 93 million miles from earth. If the sun is directly overhead, a square metre of our planet would be receiving 1 kilowatt of energy; in practice it is often cloudy, or the sun is at an angle, or simply not available – at night. The 'normal' square metre receives only 150 watts from the sun. Much of this solar energy, as heat, drives the so-called 'weather engine': if this, in turn, can be tapped, then we already have one source of power. Solar energy also grows plants which can be turned into useful power by burning, for example wood fuel, or by eating, in which case they sustain the muscle-power of men and animals. Millions of years ago, sun-sustained forests and organisms lived which were eventually buried and have become the 'fossil fuels', coal, and oil.

2 Horse plough: going about its time-honoured business under a threatening winter sky of the late 1930's. The more productive motor tractor had made its debut in the Great War, and by 1970 Great Britain had the world's heaviest tractor density: one to every 35 acres of arable land—power to produce food. Recently, F. M. L. Thompson has pointed out some of the snags of the romantic horse-powered era; in 1902 when the horse population reached its $3\frac{1}{2}$ million peak, British horses alone needed 15 million acres to supply their feed, and they made 10 million tons of manure per year.

Direct Solar Energy

From time to time attempts have been made to harness solar energy directly, not via plants or animals or the raging elements. It is said that the ancient Greek scientist Archimedes devised a system of mirrors which reflected the sun's rays on to the enemy Roman fleet at Syracuse (214 B.C.) with devastating effect. More recently, the scientist Herschel constructed a solar stove (1837), and there was a 2½ h.p. solar-fired steam engine made in Bombay in 1875. In the United States of America solar stoves have been made in quantity since about 1950, and a few solar furnaces have been constructed. Solar energy has been used for air-conditioning, water heating and even driving a car. But it is only economically promising in hot, cloudless climates, or in space exploration, and is of slight importance to the British power problem.

Wind Power

On the other hand, the sun as a generator of wind (by heating the earth and causing warm air to rise) has been of great value to Britain in the past. At first wind was used to propel ships, and it remained the main source of maritime energy (**3**) until the mid-nineteenth century: it was not until 1904 that the number of steamships overtook that of sailing ships. To a trading power like

3 Wind power: a sailing ship (the *Eclipse* of 1902) one of eight 3,000 ton four-masted steel barques belonging to the Anglo-American Oil Co., and used to bring oil from the Far East to England—a traditional power method being used to serve a very new one.

4 Wind power: a windmill pump of the type once extensively used to drain the fens; the diagram shows the simple machinery that turned the 'weather engine' into useful mechanical power. A mill could generate about 30 hp, and the sails (called 'sweeps' South of the Thames) turned at 12–20 rpm.

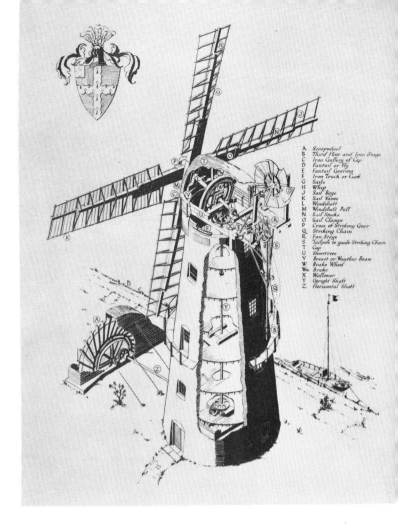

A   Scoopwheel
B   Third Floor and Iron State
C   Iron Gallery of Cap
D   Fantail or Fly
E   Fantail Gearing
F   Iron Truck or Curb
G   Sails
H   Whip
J   Sail Bays
K   Sail Vanes
L   Windshaft
M   Windshaft Poll
N   Sail Stocks
O   Sail Clamps
P   Cross of Striking Gear
Q   Striking Chain
R   Fan Stage
S   Tailpole to guide Striking Chain
T   Cap
U   Sheertrees
V   Breast or Weather-Beam
W   Brake Wheel
Ww   Brake
X   Wallower
Y   Upright Shaft
Z   Horizontal Shaft

Great Britain the convenience of strong sea-winds was a major economic fact.

The wind was also harnessed to drive windmills, and these were generally used for grinding corn or pumping out waterlogged agricultural land, so that more of the fuel could be grown. It is important to note the obvious that often escapes us: fuel and energy are the roots of our civilisation and culture, and dominate more of our activity than we usually realise. Traditionally it has been assumed that windmills were a Mediterranean area invention, discovered for the first time by travellers from the British Isles when they were on the Third Crusade (1189–92). One of the earliest definite records of an English mill is in the evidence of a dispute (1191) between Abbot Samson of Halberden, who owned a watermill, and one Dean Herbert who wanted to erect a windmill, thereby weakening the Abbot's power-monopoly. At once one has struck an elemental aspect of power-generation: a monopoly of power gives its owners great economic and social significance, for which reason the State keeps a sharp eye on such matters – a fact noted in various places throughout this book.

By the eighteenth century the local grinding mill was an integral part of the rural scene, often dominant because it had to be placed on a high or exposed place; like the power stations and gasworks of later years, they were hard to ignore. As Longfellow put it:

Behold! a giant am I!
Aloft here in my tower . . .
And the wind, the wind in my sails
Louder and louder roars.

In East Anglia where windmills drove pumps, they could be seen crowded along the great 'drains' as the irrigating channels were called. It was an attractive picture, the many wind-engines turning in what Carlyle called the 'dropsical' countryside of the Fens. The writer, William Cobbett, described such a scene in the 1830s when there was a maximum of about 10,000 windmills: 'A fine morning, the wind was brisk, and their twirling altogether added greatly to the beauty of the scene.'

Windmills were of three types, broadly differentiated by regions: post mills in Suffolk, smock mills in Kent and tower mills in Lincolnshire and the Isle of Ely. The post mill was the oldest type and would have been the sort to annoy Abbot Samson of Halberden. In good condition a mill ground ten bushels an hour. Dependent on the mills, and vice-versa, was the millwright, who used a technical jargon more lovely and quaint than those familiar today; he might be 'brigging the spindle' or fixing a 'cross-tailed gudgeon' so that the miller could 'joggle his screen'. This language like the scenic mills, grew naturally and was charmingly varied. Modern power-sources, like gasworks, have (so some aesthetes insist) intruded on nature and added to the alienation of industrial civilisation, although this is a debatable point.

Industrial civilisation killed the windmills, at any rate. By 1957 there were only thirty millers left, and once thickly-milled Suffolk declined thus: 1926: thirty-six mills; 1941: eight; 1954: four. In 1919 there were 350 working wind-mills in Britain, but by 1954 only twenty-one. How could an output of ten bushels an hour, dependent on fickle winds, compete with giant steam mills which were fed with immense quantities of grain from the prairies? The total number of mills began to fall as soon as port-based steam mills arrived; from 36,000 in 1851 to 23,000 in 1881. By 1951 it was said that the London steam mills ground enough flour for 2,200 million pounds of bread a year! Windmills could not compete with such power. Nevertheless, it was the windmill which was among the first clear attempts to 'enlarge man', to give him power to do more, and it succeeded well in its day.

The day of wind power is certainly not over. Wind pumps still help many farmers to get water, and the winds propel the increasing number of pleasure yachts which carry the leisured beneficiaries of our present 'age of power'. Even in 1948 there were investigations into the feasibility of wind-powered electrical generators, and an experimental 100 kW machine was actually erected at Costa Head in the Orkneys, where there is no shortage of wind!

5 Water power: Coalbrookdale ironworks in 1788, a pioneer plant which used water power for hammering and actuating bellows to give a better blast to the furnaces.

Water Power

While wind power has been eclipsed by its rivals, water power, the other sun-derived 'natural power', has enjoyed a remarkable rebirth, by means of hydro-electricity. However, direct water-powered mills have declined as surely as windmills. Watermills are older than windmills, and it is recorded in the Domesday Survey (1085) that there were 7,500 of them in England then. Their location was more strictly dictated than that of windmills, and they were at the mercy of frozen or dried-up rivers. Nevertheless, in the early eighteenth century there were some 27,000 watermills in Great Britain. In the Middle Ages they performed the predictable task of grinding corn, often being built and leased for the purpose by landowners; for example, the watermill at Birling, Kent – leased in the fourteenth century for 50p a year, and 300 eels from the millstream. Although they were not used for drainage, watermills, unlike windmills, had widespread use in heavy industry far into the nineteenth century.

Their earliest industrial use was working trip-hammers which in turn were used in metal forging; similarly there were a large number of water-powered cloth fulling mills. In Devon and Cornwall they helped to pump the tin and copper mines dry; at the Great Consols mine, Tavistock, in 1849, there were six-and-a-half miles of leats (artificial water channels) and a reservoir feeding the great watermill with its 40-foot diameter wheel – this mill generated 140 h.p. and lifted 52,000 lb of water at each stroke! This type of machinery represents the majestic zenith of the palaeotechnic era (the dawn of the technical age)

13

6 Tide power: one of the four proposed Severn barrages, in this case the 1924 one. Note secondary hydro-electric scheme near Chepstow, and emphasis on newly located industries; a shipyard and a super-trading estate. Technically excellent, such schemes run into serious financial problems because of their immense first cost. The Severn has a big range of tide.

which was already merging into a period of coal gas, steam engines and technical refinement.

In the closing part of water power's long innings its peculiarities had great and lasting effects on our way of life. The early cotton mills (from about 1770 onwards) were placed near swift streams. Thus the fast Pennine rivers became the arteries of the early industrial revolution. Richard Arkwright, the first modern industrialist, put his cotton mills at Cromford and Belper on the River Derwent. At a census taken in 1805 the River Wandle (South London) powered a wide variety of watermills attached to factories: twelve calico mills, nine flour, five snuff, three bleaching, three oil, two dyestuffs, one each of paper, skinning, logging, copper and iron, and also one brewery. Until the 1840s the watermill held its own, but thereafter the steam engine was unquestioned master of industrial power: it did not depend on the elements and was capable of great refinement in efficiency and power output. Later, gas and oil engines drove further gaps 'through the thinning ranks' of watermills, as they did to windmills too. As more steam mechanics were trained, so a businessman was encouraged to try the new type of power; as fewer millwrights were available, so he abandoned watermills.

14

In this way long-term changes (secular trends) generate their own catalysts or accelerators, a process which hit the steam engine in due course.

Tide Mills
A curious variation of the watermill is one operated by the tides, either a source of power to turn a wheel, or to fill a reservoir, or 'millpond'. Tidemills declined with watermills, and by 1938 there were only thirty. They suffered from the awkward working hours imposed by the tides; the Hayle tidemill in Cornwall closed because there was no local labour willing to fit in with the dictates of sun and moon when more regular work was available. Various plans for barrages across the Severn, the Wash, Morecambe Bay or the Solway Firth have occasionally embodied the tidemill idea, but so far it has remained no more than an interesting variation of great potential.

Hydro-Electricity
Before electric power was commonly available (about 1910 onwards) some private houses and factories erected their own watermill-generators. Really the machinery comprised a water turbine, although one such machine, the Pelton wheel, is a superior water wheel in effect. The first house lit by hydro-electricity was in 1880 – that of the armaments magnate, Lord Armstrong. Another installation was at Bateman's, the Sussex home of Rudyard Kipling who was a great enthusiast for things mechanical, and maintained his own domestic system. The Giant's Causeway Tramway in Northern Ireland pioneered hydro-electric power for industrial purposes (1883) when it harnessed the River Bush to drive two turbines. In Scotland, the British Aluminium Co. built a hydro-electric plant at Foyers in 1896 and another at Kinlochleven, Argyll, in 1908. Remote or mountainous country with good rainfall was an essential if hydro-electric power were to have promise; another early scheme was at, for example, Dolgarrog near Llandudno (1907) which also had an aluminium works.

Water-generated electric power now accounts for one-fiftieth of Britain's electricity. The proportion is small, but Britain's climate and topography is not the most ideal for hydro-electric development – unlike, say Norway, Canada or Switzerland. Most hydro-electric 'potential' is in Wales and Scotland, although schemes have been developed elsewhere, for example at Chester in 1913 and at York in 1923. The really major steps in making hydro-electricity a source of large public electricity supply were: the Falls of Clyde scheme (1927); Maentwrog, North Wales (1928) and the Galloway scheme (1929–35). These developments were carried out by enterprising private electricity undertakings.

In 1943, however, the state-owned North of Scotland Hydro-Electric Board was set up to develop the hydro-electric power of the Highlands, a plan which was beyond the means of any organisation but the state. By 1948 it had built five power stations (fifty-four today) and was supplying over 203,000 consumers (over 444,000 today), so justifying the enterprise of its founders. Similarly, in the

15

7, 8 Hydro-electricity: Stonebyres generating station, part of the Falls of Clyde scheme (1924–7). Already society was becoming environment-conscious, and Parliament decreed that the power houses were to be discreet and harmonious, as this shows. Inside Stonebyres are two English Electric alternators, very neat and clean as a power source compared with coal based methods (see 45, 57).

Republic of Ireland (then the Irish Free State) the great Shannon hydro-electric scheme was launched by the state in 1925–29. These two schemes emphasise the absolute importance of industrial energy to society, and the steps the state may have to take to ensure that it is available, sometimes by entering a field that purely private enterprise could not consider – over £300 million has been invested in the NSHEB, for example.

Muscle Power

In spite of the many advanced ways of generating and distributing power that are now available, for most of the half million or so years during which men, or at least hominoid creatures, have walked the earth, sheer muscle power has moved the plough, chopped the tree and generally done the work. Indeed, the artificially-generated power of today is still directed by our muscles, which shift the appropriate levers and switches at the right moment, or by holding an electric drill, for example, guide the powered apparatus. Over half of the world's population still relies on its own, or its animals' muscles, for virtually all power.

9   A Horse Gin or Whim: another version of 'power for power', from an illustration in L. Simonin's *Mines and Miners* (1869)—it could depict a scene in any of the previous four centuries. The horse walked round and round, winding coals up the shaft, simple but hopelessly slow, keeping the industry and the society dependent on it cramped and limited.

11 Power history in a nutshell: a sketch from the late 1920's when the national grid was being built; animal power at the very end of its five-thousand year epoch next to 132 kV transmission lines; past and future in one vignette.

Only the industrial and technically-advanced world has ready supplies of energy which give it 'commercial supremacy' as Thwaite called it (p. 5). Really this generation and control of great power is what makes it the 'advanced world'.

Animals have been used to further man's power potential in a variety of ways. Horses, dogs or reindeer may pull vehicles about or work machinery like horsegins (**9**). Other animals, like elephants for instance, may even lever weights with great intelligence and adroitness, or like sheep dogs, control other animals. Men have themselves carried out countless tasks by direct action. The old problem of storing energy has proved difficult with muscle power; clockwork (**10**) is one familiar way in which it has been done, and the archer's bow, when drawn, another. Clearly, however, no numerous, industrial or highly sophisticated society could be sustained long by the 'sweat of the brow', humping, horses, dogs and clockwork. Great oceans of energy must be tapped in order to do this, such as those locked in coal-beds, oil-fields or fissile material. Broadly speaking, it is man's ability to do this that has brought him to his present level and type of culture.

FURTHER READING
Solar energy is described in D. S. Halacy, *Power From The Sun*; there are many good books on windmills, a short introduction is J. N. T. Vince's *Discovering Windmills*; more advanced is Rex Wailes' *The English Windmill*. On watermills and hydro-electric power see Geoffrey Gerard *Book of Water Power*, C. P. Skilton *British Windmills and Watermills*, and *Water Power* by R. B. Way and N. D. Green. See also L. F. Syson, *British Water Mills*, and Rex Wailes, *Tide Mills*.

10 *Opposite*: Clockwork: a way of storing muscle-power; here is the machinery which drives Big Ben, the world's most famous timepiece, and still the most accurate giant clock. It was made in 1854–9 to the designs of Sir E. Beckett Denison QC (later Lord Grimthorpe). Hand-wound until 1913 (when an electric motor was attached), it required thirty hours of winding per week, although Denison had proposed automatic winding actuated by the weight of people walking over Westminster Bridge. Strictly *Big Ben* is the bell, the whole being the *Westminster Palace Clock*.

19

3 The Fossil Fuels – (I) Coal

The bulk of energy used in modern, industrial times has been obtained by burning various fuels, either directly, as in an open grate, or indirectly via such machines as steam engines or internal combustion engines. In pre-industrial times direct burning was the rule. This method was wasteful and unable to power many processes; still, the energy requirements of its users were small and simple. The usual fuels were wood, animal dung, coal (and its near relations, turf and lignite) and vegetable or animal oil.

Coal and oil dominate all other primary fuels, and historically coal has been the more important. They dominate because of their relative abundance, accessibility, convenience and calorific value. This concentration of energy for a given weight of coal is illustrated by the fact that to obtain the same amount of heat as coal, eight to eighteen times the amount of peat would have to be employed. Only the relatively greater accessibility of peat might induce men to use it: such conditions are to be found in Ireland where peat is locally superior to coal as a primary fuel.

Great Britain was economically fortunate in that it lay on immense reserves of coal, fairly easy to mine, given simple technology, and similarly easy to transport by water or rail. Coal proved to be the 'universal fuel' of the Industrial

12 A typical forest and swamp of the carboniferous era (280 million years ago; lasting some 50–60 million years) the principal age in which the coal measures were formed.

Revolution and for a long time after – certainly until 1914. It was used in heating homes, generating coal-gas and electricity, powering steam engines in ships or on railways. The Victorian age could be called (although it is now something of a catchphrase) the age of coal, or of steam.

Although London was for centuries the largest single market for coal, local industries grew up on coal fields, particularly iron-making (in West Cumberland for instance), and engineering on the North-East coast. Because these heavy or 'capital' industries were the main industries of the age the whole economy was said to be 'coal-based', hence talk of 'King Coal' or 'carboniferous capitalism'. But since 1920 it has been more or less in decline; both it and the regions dependent on it have had to undergo painful readjustment. Other sources of power have displaced King Coal. This is particularly so if seen as a world-wide phenomenon: the loss of export markets was coal's hardest blow in its first period of decline from 1920 to 1940. The loss of home markets has caused the second phase, since about 1955. The other primary fuels (oil, natural gas, nuclear energy) have proved to be cheaper or more convenient. Coal is still a large industry, and 164 million tons of it was mined in 1968. However, today it is *a* fuel, not *the* fuel.

Coal types and their Distribution
'Coal' is a general term for a number of related primary fuels. Specifically there is *lignite*, a soft brown coal not much found in Great Britain, although there is

13 The Coalman: a coal wagon carrying the fuel in 1-cwt sacks (1916). The coal was often deposited into house cellars via 'coal holes' in the pavement, a dusty and dirty business. Now most fuel comes 'by wire' or in gas pipes, or by oil tanker.

some in Ireland. The orthodox coal is *bituminous coal* which itself varies widely in type and quality. For instance, at one end of the scale is cannel coal (i.e. candle coal) with low heating, but good lighting quality. It was once held in high favour by the gas industry when coal-gas was the principal type of artificial light, and before the invention of the incandescent mantle (see page 51). At the other end is the hard near-anthracite or 'steam coal' of South Wales, a strong favourite when steam-powered engines moved the world's ships and railway trains.

Both cannel and steam coal obviously suffered when technology found better ways of lighting, and of powering transport. There were coals for standard gas, domestic hearths and general locomotive work (for those who could not afford 'best Welsh steam coal'). The hardest of all coals (i.e. nearest to pure carbon) is *anthracite*, largely a Welsh product, clean, efficient and expensive. *Coke* is simply baked coal, favoured by the Iron and Steel industry and consumers who want a smokeless fuel. Knowing all the different types of coal, and their daily fluctuating prices was an arcane subject. Its practitioners were to be found on 'coal exchanges' such as the one at Newcastle Upon Tyne. In such places one heard of Shilbottle Doubles, Naworths, Tunnel 9 ft No. 1 C, Best Hard Yorks, etc.

The coal itself is found in layers or 'seams' which vary from razor thin films to forty feet thick in Great Britain, at least. It is dug from mines that can go deeper than 3,000 ft – although much less is the rule. Until the Coal Royalties Act of 1938 coal belonged to whoever owned the surface land above it – he would be called a 'coalowner'. Either he himself worked the coal or, more likely, a colliery which paid him a 'royalty' – a levy of so much per ton extracted; usually a lease of the right to dig or 'win' the coal had to be bought as well. In 1938 all underground coal was nationalised, although the colliery companies remained independent until 1946. So one learns of the lease granted in 1356 by the Prince-Bishop of Durham for working coal at Whickham for twelve years at a rental of 500 marks (£333·33) per annum; but, to make sure that the lessees did not work the pits bare and leave nothing behind, the lease stipulated a maximum output of one keel (or barge load of twenty tons) per day. Five hundred years later leases had become very complicated documents covering such details as internal transport for the colliery, and whether the lessee could use free coal to power his own winding gear.

The main British coal fields are, or have been, widely scattered. In Scotland there was Ayrshire, the Central Belt, Fife, the Lothians. In England, Northumberland and Durham, West Cumberland, Lancs, Notts–Derby–Yorks (by 1930 the largest producer: this field accounts for forty-eight per cent of output today), North and South Staffs, Forest of Dean, Bristol and Somerset, Kent. In Wales, the North Wales field, around Wrexham; South Wales and Monmouthshire. On the other hand Ireland has little good quality coal, and although there have been workings, especially in Co. Roscommon, an absence of coal was a major factor in preventing large-scale industrialism in Ireland during the nineteenth century. There were many interesting minor fields, and remote

14 Coal in Kent: Shakespeare Colliery, Dover; the unsuccessful pioneer pit (1897–1903) of the Kent field, Britain's last such development. Deposits were found here while working on the Channel Tunnel. Note rows of 'tubbing' to line the main shafts. Other coal mines were opened in Kent, but it has always remained a small field. Note French coast on horizon. In 1971 vast reserves were discovered in Oxfordshire, some 2,000 ft. deep.

satrapies of the greater ones; for instance coal was extracted on the Mull of Kintyre from the early 1800s until 1930, and the great North-East field had an isolated outpost in the wilds of Kielder Forest, at Plashetts. It often surprises people still to learn that Kent, the 'garden of England', and the heart of bucolic Somerset near Radstock, could both boast respectable coal fields.

Continuous prospecting for new fields has gone on for years, and at least two fields owe their existence to a geologist's 'hunch'. The South-East coalfield was suggested in 1846, and searched for with great diligence over a large area. Eventually a coal seam was found near Dover in 1890 (**14**). Another lucky discovery was the second Bristol field, found as a result of geological 'sleuthing' by the self-taught geologist Handel Cossham. He found a further twenty million tons of coal (1884) and, pleasant to record, profited by it.

The Coal-Based Economy

Although the first mention of coal fuel in Britain in the records of Holyrood Abbey, Edinburgh, is about A.D. 1200, it is generally accepted that coal was known long before, in Roman Britain. Certainly the classical world as such knew of it: Theophrastus (second century B.C.) described: 'brittle stones . . . which become . . . burning coals when put into a fire'. Early fields were those which had seams very near to the surface, and the southern shore of the Firth of Forth was such a place. It is said that this coal, exported to London by sea, gave rise to the old term for the fuel, 'sea-coal' – although a similar claim is made for the Northumberland–Durham field. As a matter of interest, coal pebbles washed on to the beach are still gathered in North-East England, and represent part of an unbroken tradition of simple coal-winning going back over seven hundred years.

Early coal mines were really pits, sometimes lined with timber, or they were 'adits', short tunnels driven into the hillside. They suffered from frequent water-logging and the emission of dangerous gases. Therefore, by, say, 1700 the need for three basic technological aids was very clearly apparent: pumping, ventilation and hoisting apparatus. Coal was in great demand, and rich rewards awaited coal operators who could invent or employ these aids. Once the deeper reserves of coal could be tapped, abundant fuel would stimulate the economy, hence the importance of the inventions when they came.

As mentioned, much of the coal mined in early times went to London where it was popular for domestic and simple industrial use (breweries, blacksmiths, soap boilers, etc.). But it had unpleasant side-effects for the community at large, in particular giving off dirty smoke. Thus one person's personal convenience became what economists call an 'external diseconomy' for everybody else, and atmospheric pollution joined the refuse problem as one of the basic problems of urban civilisation. The problem led to government action, and in 1306 Edward I ordered all London blacksmiths to desist from using coal. The popular domestic market was so large that successive governments preferred to avoid taking rigorous action; instead they taxed coal, following a well-worn path of fiscal common sense, that the state should enjoy at least part of new sources of prosperity – in the manner that it taxes petrol today. The main coal taxes lasted until 1831.

Mining developed in other coal fields than Fife, the Lothians and North-East England to satisfy the local or London markets. For instance, the rent roll of Lord Lincoln in the fourteenth century lists a coal mine near Colne (Lancs), and John Leland who toured England (1540) noted a Mr Bradshaw's cannel and sea-coal mine near Wigan. The Royal Kingswood Chase charter of 1223 mentions the digging of sea-coal near Bristol, and similar charters and rent-rolls paint a picture of widespread if patchy mining by 1700, the North-East coast still enjoying the lion's share. On the other hand there are also an increasing number of unfriendly references to the use of coal which tell of increasing use and pollution from the consumer's point of view. John Evelyn in his diary (1670) spoke of London with its 'hellish and dismal cloud of sea coal . . . the inhabitants breathe nothing but an impure and thick mist accompanied with a . . . filthy vapour . . . corrupting the lungs'.

15 Auld Reekie: i.e. 'old smoky', Edinburgh before the 1956 Clean Air Act. Open coal-burning grates gave cheap heat to large urban areas, but in a heavy price in 'amenity'; B. H. Thwaite wrote (1896) 'our cities are almost unfit to live in—the natural life of a Zulu is to be preferred to that of a city worker, amidst the dirty ˉsurroundings of our smoke begrimed cities'. Such conditions blackened buildings, added to the housewives' burden and induced chest illness—especially bronchitis.

Occasionally a petition was organised against the menace (as in 1648) and the government was prodded into some cursory action, but the benefits of sea coal were great, and no other fuel was available to fight the rigours of winter, or to bake, boil and brew at tens of thousands of hearths. In 1580 London imported 15,000 tons of sea-coal, by 1700 it imported 323,000 tons: two-fifths of the output of the North-East coast. The Scottish field generally served its home market, notably Edinburgh (**15**) and was encouraged to do so by the Scottish Parliament (1600) which observed that coal was 'growand scant daily' and put an embargo on exports.

However, plenty of new fields were developed to satisfy growing demands from London and elsewhere. By the 1750s sea-coal was sent to numerous minor ports, or even dumped on beaches where there was no good harbour, as at Hastings. Glamorgan coal fed North Devon, Flint and Cumberland supplies the North-West coast, and London's Tyneside suppliers also landed coal along the shores of Kent and Sussex. Where they could get it, the primitive industries of 'pre-industrial' Britain used coal, but they had to be near a coal working or a port. Otherwise they used wood, like the Wealden iron industry. However, the increasing use of coal was sufficiently great in the seventeenth century that one historian has seen the period as a real 'industrial revolution' – a view frequently rejected as an exaggeration in view of the unique and stupendous achievements of 1780–1840 and beyond.

On these sturdy if dwarfish foundations the astounding 'age of coal' was to flourish in the nineteenth century. Statistics show this clearly:

Output of Coal: until 1800 figures are for the North-East coast only; thereafter they are national. They are in *millions of tons.*

1660:	0·65	1913:	287·4 (all-time peak)
1752:	1·2	1920:	229·5
1800:	10·0 (N.E. coast: 2·1)	1930:	243·9
1854:	64·7	1940:	224·3
1870:	110·4	1950:	216·7
1880:	147·0	1960:	193·6
1890:	181·6	1968:	164·1
1900:	225·2	1975:	120·0 (estimate)

This swift expansion up to 1913 resulted from important changes in the methods of producing coal, and a rapid growth of markets: supply and demand seemed to grow automatically, although the story was to be very different after 1919. The developments on the supply side were as follows:

Geology: in the nineteenth century some remarkable minds revolutionised this science (MacCulloch, Murchison, Sedgwick, Lyell, etc.) thereby making the discovery of coal reserves easier; an official geological survey started in 1835. However, newly-discovered coal measures were often deep, and so improved *pumping* was necessary as deep mines often flood with water from the surrounding water-bearing rocks. Early miners sometimes used drainage tunnels, or conduits from the workings to a nearby river if sufficient inclination rendered this possible. Latter-day drainage tunnels could be quite large, e.g. one running from Kenton to Scotswood on Tyne for two miles in 1770. Crude horse-driven pumps are also recorded (Finchale Priory on the River Wear, 1486). The first 'technological breakthrough' was Savery's steam pump in 1698, closely followed by the more potent Newcomen engine of 1705 – early versions of this machine could lift water 150 feet, thereby allowing deeper working and the tapping of new reserves.

Better than all these engines was Watt's revolutionary and famous steam engine (*c.* 1778) which could generate more power for less fuel than its earlier rivals, roughly 3 lb of coal per h.p./hour as opposed to a good Newcomen on 32 lb per h.p./hour. By 1800 there were about 1,200 steam pumps of all kinds at work, and they released a supply blockage of coal, occasioned by the repeated flooding of pits ('coal was the lifeblood of the industrial economy, and with the progressive introduction of hundreds of engines its circulation improved from the lethargic to the lively' (J. R. Harris in *History*, June 1967)). After Watt, other engineers produced more refined engines, notably Cornish engineers who had an eye to fuel economy, and later still electric pumps took over drainage work (from 1882 onwards).

Drainage in deep mines is only one natural problem, there are others: *ventilation* and *lighting.* Deep mines are hot and stuffy, they fill with dangerous gases from the coal seams, and they are totally dark. The most urgent problem is the existence of lethal or potentially explosive gases, such as fire-damp (CH_4), after-damp (CO_2) and choke-damp (CO) and the fog of coal dust which accompanies working, and which can behave like an explosive gas; one of the worst accidents ever (Hulton, Lancs, 1910 – 344 killed) was so caused. In the earliest pits miners 'beat out' gas by flapping blankets at it, a rather ineffectual method. The first effective cure was to sink two shafts into the mine and light a fire at the top of one. The resulting up-draught drew air down the clear shaft and kept some circulation going. This method was in operation by 1700, but it was hard to control and not very potent. The true solution lay in mechanical (i.e. pumped or fanned) ventilation, which was slowly adopted from 1810. Better machines shifted more air and allowed deeper workings: an air pump of 1835 might move 5,000 cubic feet of air per minute, whereas a 'Sirocco' fan of 1925 could move 400,000 cubic feet per minute, and render a coal mine a more congenial place of work.

Early mine lighting was by naked candle, or by a shower of sparks struck from a flint-and-wheel, the latter being marginally safer than a candle, but not very bright. The single famous invention which improved mine illumination was the safety lamp, invented by George Stephenson and Sir Humphry Davy (1815). Electric lighting started in 1882.

Better lamps and ventilation helped to reduce the frequency of terrible accidents in coal mines. Mines still remained very dangerous, and a very high price in human life was exacted in getting the lifeblood for the 'Workshop of the World', as men called industrial Britain. A selection of mine disasters display this: Brandling Colliery, 1812 (92 dead); Newbottle, 1815 (63); Wallsend, 1835 (102); St Hilda, South Shields, 1839 (52); Haswell, 1844 (95); New Hartley, 1862 (204) and Seaham, 1880 (52) – and these accidents were in the North-East coast field alone. The more exacting standards of later years, usually imposed by the state, reinforced improved technology in drastically reducing mining accidents. However, disquieting evidence of human error, slackly-observed regulations and penny-pinching by managers came to light in enquiries relating to accidents. Suspicion remains that such awful disasters as Whitehaven, 1910 (136) and Senghenydd, 1913 (439) could have been avoided if regulations had been observed, and as late as Gresford, Denbigh, 1934 (265) there was enough evidence to institute legal proceedings against the management.

There were many other technical improvements to coal mining which backed the great advances in pumping, lighting, etc. For example, the first mines sent their coal to the surface by simply humping it on men's, or often women's, backs; later came the horsegin (**9**) and finally the winding engine (1800 onwards). As these engines became more powerful, so could the output of a pit rise: in 1835 the maximum was about 300 tons per twelve hours, by 1850 it was 800 tons. The general application of electric power to coal mines accelerated the application of power to further processes, such as underground power-cutting of coal, and mechanical haulage on underground tramways. Compressed

16 Patent Fuel: The first 'patent' for making fuel (processed coal, giving off less or no smoke) was in 1799. Here are the Neath Abbey patent fuel works (1921) at a time when Britain used 2.3 million tons of it per year: the total has only risen to 3.8 million tons (1968) and the works shown closed *c.* 1930. The improved performance of patent fuel has had to battle with its higher costs, and with rival primary and secondary fuels.

air was used as a flexible power medium even earlier (1849) and remained very popular because of its complete safety. The spread of powered mining was slow, however – and far slower than in the case of Britain's rivals; in 1913 only twenty-three million tons out of the total 287 million tons was power-cut. Above ground the coal could be screened (1770 onwards) into various sizes for different markets; it could be coked in a gas works (p. 47) or pulverised into 'patent fuel' briquettes (**16**) which appeared from 1800 onwards. Finally canals and then railways transferred the coal quickly and cheaply to the rapidly-growing markets.

The demand for coal seemed insatiable; it was the result of the growth of a variety of industries and economies dependent on it. It was, moreover, world-wide: British coal powered Italian and Argentine steam trains, and steamers in the Indian Ocean – this was one important factor in the creation of a world-economy which in turn has led men to speculate about the possibility of a genuine world-society or 'global village'. The most obvious industrial user of coal was the burgeoning iron and steel industry; then the 22,000-mile railway network which was kept mobile by coal alone. Coal made the gas which lit and occasionally heated Victorian homes, it burnt in millions of domestic grates and supplied useful by-products (aniline dyes, for instance, in 1856). It was exported as 'bunker coal' and could be seen piled into black heaps at 'coaling stations' like Aden. Coal ports, places like Maryport, Whitehaven, Methil and Amble, their air always tasting of black dust, disgorged up to ninety-seven million tons of coal per year (1913) and enjoyed long-forgotten prosperity.

The Long Decline

Coal's pre-1914 prosperity rested on fragile foundations, however. Even the Victorians expressed doubts sometimes. In 1865 an economist, Stanley Jevons, foresaw a time when easily-worked seams would be exhausted and (given fixed or growing demand) prices would rise. By 1900 he was being proved right; seams were running out, and in order to win coal from more difficult ones the coalowners simply employed more and more men. This process was expensive; a wiser course would have been to mechanise more intensively, as did the USA or Germany. Instead, the industry became *labour-intensive*: in 1900 there were

632,000 miners producing 227 tons per man per year, by 1913 there were 1·1 million miners producing 247 tons – by 1920 it was down to 199 tons, after which productivity (output per man) rose with belated mechanisation. In economic terms all this displayed the Law of Diminishing Returns – that, broadly speaking, after a given point there can be a situation where one gets 'less with more', thereby reversing Fuller's doctrine (p. 7). Extractive industries like coal mining are especially prone to this. Also, there was, by world standards, an uncomfortably large number of men working in archaic pits, two-thirds of all coal coming, by 1913, from pre-1875 mines. Coalowners were reputedly obstinate, conservative, independent and prone to complacency. A proposal to effect a really big amalgamation and rationalisation of coal mines (1893) fell on stony ground, so while the Ruhr had twelve large mining companies, Britain had over 1,000, and many of these were inefficient.

After 1919 came the reckoning, for the coalowners could no longer pass on their high costs to a large, captive market. Above all, foreign customers were lost, for they now developed hydro-electricity or their own coalfields, or simply used the oil-burning internal combustion engine as a prime mover. In any case the world economy was unstable and, from 1929 to 1932, acutely depressed, a factor which not only lost overseas markets, but depressed home demand. The home market stagnated at about 184 million tons instead of going 'onward and upward' as in the pre-1914 era. Greater efficiency in the use of coal meant that less was used for a given amount of energy generated; for example, between 1920 and 1930 the amount of electricity obtained from a given amount of coal doubled, and in 1932 the Coal Utilisation Council was founded to press for greater fuel economy. All these things meant that the growth of demand for coal fell behind the growth of the economy as a whole. In 1922 coal went to the following markets (millions of tons in brackets): Power (60); Domestic (35); Factory engines (30); Coke (20); Gas (18); Railways (15); Others (9½).

The steady loss of exports was more serious. Apart from freak years like 1922 (when there was a coal strike in the USA) it fell steadily from nearly 100 million tons in 1913 to twenty-four million tons in 1920 when it rose to fifty million tons and hovered about there until 1939. The twin and related results of this decline in the use of coal were unemployment and the start of the 'regional problem'. From 1925–1938 never less than twenty per cent of Britain's miners were out of work, and a further 200,000 left the industry altogether. Because mining was concentrated in certain areas like Co. Durham and South Wales their suffering was acute, especially if, like South Wales, they had been heavy exporters. An area like the Rhondda Valley in the 1930s was a grim example of industrial and social dereliction. Other old and heavy industries waned at this time, too, intensifying the regional decline of, say, West Cumberland or Central Scotland. Much has been done to alleviate the regional decline of large parts of Britain, but the essential problem remains. Efforts by coalowners and the state to mollify the blow to coal had some slight effect, but the real problem was falling demand,

29

17 Power-based society: an aerial photo of Newcastle Upon Tyne, once coal-capital of the world, seen here towards the end of the coal era, (early 1950's). Note omnipresence of power in a modern society: Elswick gasworks (then coal fired): steam engines in the railway yards, and coal fired factories (notably a lead smelter by the river). Under the streets are electric power mains, and by night the scene would be illuminated artificially. The power sources change, the principle remains.

just as excess demand had been the cause of its overblown size and complacent management in the past.

After the Second World War coal still remained a major primary fuel industry. Yet after 1955 (and for the first time) it had to face a really serious challenge from rivals like oil and nuclear energy. At first, immediately after the war, demand was high and the industry was hardly able to cope. Stocks grew low, and in the severe winter of 1947 the Fuel Crisis led to rationing of coal, power cuts, industrial shut-downs resulting in two million people unemployed, and the loss of £200 million of exported manufactures. Clearly coal was still the 'lifeblood' of the economy, a fact driven home to housewives pushing prams of 'nutty slack' or sitting in front of cherry-red electric fires. They and their families would have found it hard to believe that King Coal was about to be sharply reduced in status. Resentment of the crisis led to a determination by politicians that such an affair must not recur, and subsequent fuel policies have encouraged diversification of fuels. Thus from 1950 when coal was 94.5 per cent of British primary fuel it fell to eighty per cent in 1960, to fifty-nine per cent in 1970 and to an estimated thirty-five per cent by 1975. Successive governments have kept a sharp eye out for winter fuel problems, the 1964 Labour administration even having a 'Winter Emergency Committee' of the cabinet to forestall such trouble, and journalists are ever-ready to raise the bogey of 1947 to prod governments or catch attention.

Against this sad record of decline one must note the startling increase in the efficiency and morale of the coal industry itself. Because the coal industry was once labour-intensive, it meant that a shortage of labour meant an immediate shortage of coal – one of the main reasons for the 1947 fiasco. The National Coal Board which took the industry over from the coalowners in 1947 poured large quantities of capital into coalmining, £72 million from 1947–1949 alone. Output per manshift nearly doubled from 1950–1970 as a result. Intensive training, underground mechanisation and the more continuous use of equipment have achieved this, and there is even a fully automated pit (Bevercotes, 1969) at work. Mining has been concentrated in newer and more efficient pits: there were 296 coal mines in 1970 compared with nearly 1,000 in 1947, and at the same time the number of miners has fallen from 711,000 to 300,000.

Because people are prone to exaggerate for effect, there has been loose talk of the 'collapse' of the coal industry. This is wrong: it has declined, and probably will continue to, yet it has many years of useful life left and it remains vital, also it can always expand if its rivals fail: there are vast reserves of coal left under Britain. Being an extractive industry it must *ipso facto* decline in the long run. The 'age of coal' was the age of first-generation basic industrialism; when it was over, the painful structural adjustment had to come. There is also exaggerated criticism of past enterprise. Note the words of the *Reid Report* on coal mining (1945): 'let us beware of being wise after the event, or of witholding . . . praise due to the great race of men, employers, mining engineers, workmen and machinery makers alike. For whatever their faults they were fit to rank with the greatest of Britain's industrial pioneers.'

Miners, Coalowners and the State

The miners (or 'colliers', 'pitmen', etc.) were often called the 'aristocrats of labour' in the great years of the industry. This was not only because of the national importance of the 'black diamonds' which they cut, but also because of their courage, comradeship and panache, and above all the leading rôle they took in forming trade unions and political organisations. They enjoyed a distinctive culture with own dialects (technical and regional), pit-villages and customs. The miners and their allies were a major force in winning state supervision of (and eventually acquisition of) their industry. Clearly the 'collier lads' as one of their songs called them, played a unique part in British economic and political history, and have enriched the national culture in many ways.

Because they often lived in purely coal-winning towns and villages the miners had a strong sense of community. Significantly a large proportion of the few good

31

pieces of literature about industrial life in general, and the power industries in particular (*pace* H. G. Wells' *Lord of the Dynamos*) concern miners: Llewellyn's *How Green Was My Valley*, and the stories of D. H. Lawrence. Coal-culture if it may be so termed, was enshrined in places like Mountain Ash, Tonypandy, Trimdon Grange and Sanquhar. It is associated with pitmen's choirs, the 'Miners' Gala' (pronounced 'gayla') of Durham; and although many of these things survive, their real power lies in the past when the industry that gave them birth was strong and confident. On the other hand, much of the change for which miners struggled so hard and long has come about, and is an important and normal way of life now. The first miners' trade unions were local and weak, but later (1863) they formed a loose national organisation. The strong local and individualist tradition made it difficult to organise a true national union, but this came in 1908 (the Miners' Federation, later the National Union of Mineworkers). Mining trade unionists were extremely tough negotiators, and were willing to face the spartan rigours of a strike in an age when this meant total sacrifice. Their example inspired respect, and was a strong catalyst in forming the modern trade union movement.

In 1907 one-third of trade union members were coal miners, and a large number of true 'working men MPs' too; six out of eleven in 1885 when the first sizeable contingent arrived at Westminster. The first working man MP of them all (in modern times) was Thomas Burt, who was elected by Morpeth in the North-East coalfield in 1874 as a 'Radical Labour' candidate. His fellow-miners enshrined their victory in one of the coal folk-songs: 'The Pitman gan te Parlemint'. Even in the 1966 Parliament, thirty-two of the 630 MPs represented mining areas, or were coal miners by origin. It is clear, therefore, that the miners (who, with their dependents, numbered about four millions in 1913) have been more than workers in yet another industry – they were for many years the true aristocrats of labour.

The single strongest factor in making the coal miners into a unified and organised political and social force was the harsh environment in which they toiled. Even in the coarse, brutal world of early industrialism, the starkness and cruelty of their lives shocked public opinion – if and when it got to learn of these matters. Children and women worked underground until the Mines Act (1842) forbade it. They dragged waggons of coal, crawling along on their knees; half-starved infants sat in rat-infested darkness opening and shutting ventilation doors. In return for this they might get 4d–6d (2½p) per day (Bristol coalfield, 1832). A grown man might earn 10s (50p) per week, out of which he had to sustain his family; bread was 1s (5p) per loaf in coal areas, after which came rent, fuel, clothing, etc. A pitman's suit cost £1 in 1850, and was a functional outfit worn until the early twentieth century: 'boots, heavy blue stockings, breeches cut off at the knees and split so that they might be drawn over boots; a heavy wool waistcoat and jacket' (Frank Atkinson, *The Great Northern Coalfield*).

We know many of these facts from the major government enquiry into mining conditions which was undertaken in 1840, and out of which came the Mines Act. Government inspectors found little girls working in Cumberland pits at 6d per day, and the mule-drivers at Willington, Co. Durham, 'frequently vomiting in the ill-ventilated galleries' of a mine which netted profits of £17,000 per year. This difference between the hard driven and impoverished pitmen, and the swelling profits of the coal owners was a major grievance, and corroded labour relations for over a century. It fascinated Benjamin Disraeli, novelist and politician (later Prime Minister) who had such matters in mind when he wrote *Sybil* (1845) in which he spoke of the 'Two Englands' – the rich and the poor, so far apart that they might have lived on different planets. He described 'a wilderness of cottages and tenements . . . scattered over the land . . . interspersed with blazing furnaces, heaps of burning coal and piles of smouldering ironstone . . . (where) . . . in the twilight hour . . . they came forth: the mill delivers its gang and the pit its bond-men . . . the swarming multitude . . . wet with toil and black as the children of the tropics.' Among them were girls, from whose 'lips born to breathe words of sweetness come oaths that men might shudder at'; he went on to remark that the infants who 'emerge from the bowels of the earth' were condemned to a punishment worse than that meted out to criminals, although that particular horror had ceased three years before *Sybil* was published.

Thus it is no surprise that the British coalfields became the cradles of socialism, communism, syndicalism and other political philosophies that sought to redress the bitter sense of injustice nourished by many miners. A whole society depended upon their efforts, but seemed to reward their employers, not the underground workers themselves. George Orwell put the matter well in his classic *The Road to Wigan Pier* (1937): 'All of us *really* owe the comparative decency of our lives to poor drudges underground, blackened to the eye, with their throats full of coal dust, driving their shovels forward with arms and belly muscles of steel.'

The coalowners also pioneered collective organisation, partly to counteract the activities of their employees. Like the trade unions they were organised locally and nationally. Their national grouping was the Mining Association of Great Britain (1854), and a typical local body would be the Lanarkshire Coal Masters' Association (1886). Both owners and employees pressurised governments to favour them with legislation. Reasonable public opinion generally backed the miners, who worked in harsh conditions. In this way the oldest power industry has a long record of state intervention in order to improve conditions, guarantee wages or, in later years, enforce reorganisation. Partly, therefore, mining legislation was passed to protect the weak in the 'economic jungle' of laissez-faire capitalism. Only in the twentieth century did the state intervene in organisation, as it had done with gas and electricity from their earliest days.

Britain's transformation into a mass industrial democracy has been occasioned without undue violence and hysteria. Experience in factory and mining legislation very early on in industrial times partly accounts for this (*c.* 1830–1860); so, too, does the example and activity of the miners themselves who worked for their social and economic ends with determination and steadiness, above all with strong organisation; qualities probably engendered by the very nature of their work.

Coal Legislation

First phase: paternalism

1799 Employment Act, abolishes serfdom which had survived in some Scottish mines, e.g. Duke of Hamilton's at Corrinden near Bo'ness

1829–30 Parliamentary Committee recommends abolition of coal tax as 'a severe restriction on trade'; actually abolished 1831

1831 Truck Act: Workers (especially relevant to pitmen) to be paid in cash, not kind, at the 'company store'; weakens hold of owners

1842 Mines Act: like 1833 Factory Act, very important. No women or children ('ten or under') to work underground – nor even 'boys under fifteen to act as winding engineers'

1846 Government Commission recommends HM Inspectors of Mines (cf. 1833 Factory Act)

1850 Mines Act: Colliery managers to be qualified and four Inspectors appointed, to ensure safe working

1855 Mines Act, tightens up safety regulations

1860 Mines Act: miners may elect their own 'checkweighman' or output checker (wages based on output, therefore sensitive point)

1872 Mines Act: codifies much of above, and sets exams for managers

1887 Mines Act: minimum working age twelve, winding engineers twenty-two

1908 Eight Hour Act: eight-hour maximum working day in mines

1912 Minimum Wage Act: sets bottom level through which coal workers' wages cannot fall, a *statutory wage* (cf. Trade Board Act 1909)

Second phase: reorganisation

1916–17 Coal Act: industry temporarily run by state as a wartime measure – lasts till 1921

1919 Royal Commission (Sankey) suggests nationalisation (rejected) and seven-hour working day (accepted; Coal Mines Act 1920)

1921 Industry de-controlled, collapse of high wartime wages and prices, increasing bitterness among miners

1925–6 State subsidy of £23 million to stave off wage cuts

1926 Wage cuts, followed by seven-month strike (which in turn sparked off General Strike)

1925–6 Royal Commission (Samuel) suggests amalgamation and greater efficiency: negligible results

1930 Coal Mines Act: effects some improvement by dividing Great Britain into various producing and selling districts

1938 Coal deposits (but not mines) nationalised at a cost of £66 million

1946 Coal Industry Nationalisation Act: state takes over mines and vests them in NCB.

1946 onwards: various fuel policies, see page 91.

Turf

In Great Britain the exploitation of combustible turf has never been great, although in Ireland it has for long been a staple fuel. Much is still dug there for domestic use (about two million tons a year) although a greater proportion has been scientifically cut on a big scale (Turf Development Board of 1934, and Bord na Móna of 1946) by state-owned organisations, which manifest again the needs for national fuel policies, and state aid in so vital a national matter.

The main drawback of turf is that it requires drying before use: this can be slow, and itself absorbs energy. However, when it is plentiful and other fuels are markedly more expensive it enjoys local advantages and may be used. Ireland has as much turf, but far less coal than Great Britain, hence its popularity there. As early as 1908 there was proposed a peat-fired power station. It was not built, although some successful ones have been in recent years, the first one at Portarlington in 1950. In Great Britain turf has suffered disadvantages relative to coal and oil; there has been some commercial cutting from time to time, e.g. in North Somerset, Teesdale and on Dartmoor. Its use as a soil enricher continues, but as a fuel it has only occasional significance.

FURTHER READING

As the oldest power industry, coal has been well recorded by historians, although no really succinct and modern history has yet appeared. The rather heavy institutional history of the miners' union *The Miners* by R. Page Arnott has some very interesting material in it, for those willing to dig. A superb illustrated survey of the coal industry at its zenith (1915) recently reprinted is *The British Coal Trade* by H. S. Jevons, and another copy reprint, of an old history, is the *History of Coal Mining in Great Britain* by R. L. Galloway. An interesting account of life as seen by a political miner is *A Man's Life* by the late Lord Lawson, and a general survey of the technical and human side of one field, well illustrated, is *The Great Northern Coalfield* by Frank Atkinson. The NCB issues useful statistical data, mostly relating to contemporary problems.

4 The Fossil Fuels – (II) Oil

An arbitrary, though fair date for starting the oil era is 1850. In that year J. Young, a Scottish chemist, produced paraffin from crude mineral oil, and within ten years the first 'oil rush' had occurred in Pennsylvania, USA. Thus within a short time the twin foundations of another primary fuel industry were laid: oil could be refined into more manageable liquids, and immense quantities were shown to be available. From Britain's point of view the events were symbolic: she led the world in oil techniques, but the oil was all overseas – or virtually so. Ever since the mid-nineteenth century, civilisation has come to rely more heavily on oil for a large proportion of its heat and light. In fact, oils of various kinds had been known for ages past, and had been used to obtain light – animal fat (tallow) was the oldest source of 'oil light' and towards the end of the primitive illumination age (c. 1880) Britain produced 100,000 tons of tallow a year, importing as much again.

A large number of alternative lamp oils, and especially the better ones which burnt clear and without odour, were exotic in origin, further evidence of the traditional and heavy dependence Britain has had on foreign oil sources: rape oil from Gujerat in India; colza oil from Ichang, China; gingelly oil from the seeds of the sesame bush; oil from tea seeds, pumpkin seeds and from whales and sharks; even from alligators – a good Brazilian specimen gave twelve gallons per tail! In 1838 Britain imported just over £1 million worth of illuminating oils. Obviously a society dependent on these sources of light could not expand demand without facing serious depletion, or quickly expanded cultivation, of these somewhat tenuous origins of the oil; the situation was unstable.

As stated elsewhere, important inventions are those which are well-timed as answers to some pressing contemporary problem. The principle embodied in them may have been known before, but now it is relevant. As the 'hour made the machine' with steam-engines, or tanks and submarines, so it did with oil. The 'new' source of light was mineral oil, or petroleum. Like coal, mineral oil lay below ground level, sometimes very deep. Occasionally it seeped to the surface; the Greek Herodotus (450 B.C.) described such an oil well near Babylon, and the traveller, d'Allien (1629), tells of Red Indians using mineral oil (not as a fuel, but as a skin medicine) – early American colonists certainly did use it as a fuel, however. In Europe (in Galicia and Roumania) simple oil wells were made by digging large holes in the ground where the oil-bearing strata came near to the surface, and similar wells were dug in Burma.

This oil, if burned unrefined, generally made an unpleasant smell, like some of its processed cousins, e.g. fish-oil; also no great sources of it were known, so it was

18 *Above* Early Oil: The shale oil refinery at Uphall, Linlithgowshire (now West Lothian), note 'bings' or heaps of reddish shale waste.

19 *Below* The Royal Dutch Petroleum Co's (now part of Shell) refinery at Pangkalan Brandan in Sumatra, Dutch East Indies (now Indonesia) 1893.

not seen as an answer to the lamp oil problem. In the 1850s the oil revolution quickly altered these commonly held beliefs. Although paraffin had been known in 1830, the breakthrough was the process devised by Dr James Young of Glasgow (1850) which obtained paraffin from coal or shale. The first coal with which he had success was at Alfreton, Derbyshire, but bigger reserves of the requisite grades of coal (and of shale) were to be found in Scotland, where a shale-oil industry quickly developed. The coal workings at Torbanehill were exhausted by 1862 but the shale-oil industry survived for just a century from the opening of Robert Bell's shale oil refinery at Broxburn. The industry remained fairly localised, in the Lothians, where such concerns as the Oakbank Oil Co., and Young's Paraffin Light and Mineral Oil Co. swelled the output of indigenous fuel. Its record in the twentieth century ran thus:

Shale-Oil Output in millions of tons
1907:	2,690,028
1938:	1,551,000
1947:	1,236,000
1960:	669,000
1962:	ceased.

Contrary to popular belief that Britain has no native oil supplies, there has been some small output from British oilfields in this century, although it has been erratic and extremely modest. It has come from such wells as Gainsborough, Lincs., and Kimmeridge, Dorset, where small local fields exist. British oil has been extracted since the 1920s, but it has never been a major power source. Another native oil, dating back to Young's day, is oil from coal, which was first developed with urgency late in the First World War when foreign sources were menaced by submarine warfare. Oil thus produced is expensive and only found favour because it carried lighter taxes than normal mineral oil. When these preferential duties were abolished (1965) production of coal-based oil ceased, although it remains a possible source if cheaper conversion processes can be found. Apart from the few scanty native fields (which produce one out of every thousand tons of Britain's oil needs) overseas sources have traditionally supplied the British oil market – a possible undersea source was found some 200 miles offshore from Aberdeen (1970): if it proved fruitful it would run contrary to the historical trend recorded.

Soon after Young's discovery (and based on it) patents were taken out for refining mineral oil – as opposed to coal and shale oil – into paraffin. Already such oil was being imported from Yenangyuang in Upper Burma. In August 1859 great reserves of mineral oil were found at Oil Creek, Pennsylvania, by drilling into the ground after the manner of drilling for water. The oil was only seventy feet below the ground level, yet the important method of drilling – as opposed to digging – had been established. For ten years thereafter Pennsylvania was the

20 An early British-owned oilfield at Yenangyuang, Burma (Burmah Oil Co.)—even with transport costs, these Far Eastern oils could defeat the native British shale oil industry.

oil centre of the world, until the methods of the first drilling prospector, E. L. Drake, were copied elsewhere and yielded equal or superior results. By 1880 Russia and Roumania were producing on a large scale, and by 1895 the East Indies and Burma also.

While these large sources of oil supplied cheap paraffin, and so contributed to social progress in Britain, still no home oil fields were found. This single fact was of great importance, for it contributed in the long run to Britain's eclipse as the world's leading economic power, a process far gone by even 1914. Two further facts must be noted: from 1900 oil became an important direct source of energy (as opposed to merely lighting), through the medium of the petrol-, or oil-burning internal combustion engine. This increased the economic and political power of those who controlled the sources of oil. Also, Britain made up her deficiency as an oil producer by becoming an important developer of oilfields in other countries, and a key transporter and marketer of the fuel. In later years she became a leading refiner of oil, too.

The young oil industry tended to coalesce into big corporations which became, and remained, household names. This was partly because large amounts of capital were needed to develop pipelines, tankers, refineries, etc., and partly because the first-comers made determined efforts to dominate the lucrative

21 Coaling Ship: fuelling HMS *Iron Duke*, a battleship of 1914. The whole ship's crew had to hand-hump coal on board, only the band was excused in order to soothe the toiling sailors with music, and the wireless telegraphists whose delicate 'touch' on morse keys would be broken by excessive strain. HMS *Iron Duke* had 30,000 hp engines, fed by eight coal burning boilers; she could steam at 22 knots. The popularity of Admiral Fisher's proposal to use oil fuel is immediately understandable on seeing this picture: the whole ship had to be cleaned to perfection after each coaling.

market for oil, or at least keep a big part of it. For a long time they were single-minded and successful in their efforts, and were helped by the lack of expertise and capital among would-be new entrants. British firms like Burmah Oil (1886) (**20**) or Shell (1897) were among these first dominant organisations. American firms supplied oil to the British market, too – like Esso (= S.O.: Standard Oil), and gradually an equilibrium was reached whereby the British market was dominated by the so-called 'big seven'. Since 1945 many new firms have managed to break in, and there are now some 200 oil companies working in Britain, although the former big seven still account for sixty-four per cent of all sales. Names like 'Shell' are rather general; in fact they refer to a group of related companies which have been set up to variously produce, transport or refine the oil. Large business corporations have become a dominant feature of twentieth-century economies, and the oil giants – themselves children of the same century – are leading examples of this process.

War is a stimulant and accelerator of many economic trends. Both World Wars threw more dependence on oil as a source of power, and both were won, significantly, by those who had access to unlimited quantities of this fuel; the defeat of Germany and Japan in 1945 was measurably due to their oil shortages. The attraction of oil as a fuel for warships of the Royal Navy (**21**) gained a major new customer for the industry from 1905 onwards and represented virtually its first major victory over coal. To ensure greater control over supplies, a later First Lord of the Admiralty, Winston Churchill, persuaded the government to buy a half-share in the supplying company (today's British Petroleum), an early example of a process by which later governments have sought to influence industry. When the First World War began, the army owned 827 motor cars and fifteen motor bicycles: at the end it owned 79,000 cars and lorries and 34,000 motor bicycles, all voracious users of petrol or 'motor spirit' as it was often called. The total number of oil- and petrol-driven vehicles then began its steep climb to today's total: in 1910, 144,000; in 1923, one million; in 1935, 2½ million; in

1970, 15 million. The original oilfields mentioned were later joined by others in supplying this rapidly-growing market: Venezuela (1922), Iraq (1927) and Bahrain (1932).

As well as being a source of power, oil has been increasingly in demand for its valuable by-products, as coal has also been. As early as 1872 the Russian scientist Mendeleyev said (on seeing the Pennsylvania oilfield): 'This material is too valuable to be burned.' However, it was the Second World War that really stimulated this side of the industry, particularly in the matter of producing synthetic rubber. Oil is now a base for propane gas (itself a source of power); detergents, fertilisers, nylon, films, 'PVC' material, etc. – although only two per cent of all oil is so used.

Refineries and Pipelines

Until about 1950 most oil brought to Britain was refined at its source, and brought in tankers as actual petrol. This was relatively expensive and obviously rather dangerous, especially in wartime. Some home refineries did exist, the oldest being at Pumpherston which had been erected in 1844 to refine shale-oil. Others were at Fawley (Esso, 1921); Shell Haven (Shell, 1916); Llandarcy (BP, 1921) and Barton, near Manchester (Manchester Oil Co. – later Burmah Oil – 1938). These were all small by postwar standards, and there were only twelve of them in any case before 1940. They could refine about one-quarter of Britain's needs. After 1950 there were strong factors favouring home refining. There was the need to conserve sterling, the desire to develop a by-product industry and the wish to be independent of potentially unfriendly foreign suppliers – the latter point being sharply drawn by the Abadan crisis, 1950, when a British-owned refinery in Iran was suddenly seized. The postwar programme of refinery building really started in 1947, and has increased home capacity from $2\frac{1}{2}$ million tons (1947) to eighty-five million tons (1970). Individual refineries became much larger, and British ones were world-leaders in size, like Milford Haven (Esso, 1960), Pembroke (Texaco, 1964) or the Isle of Grain (BP, 1953).

Once the oil is pumped ashore from tankers, it can be transported about by

22 A Modern Refinery: Fawley, near Southampton, by night. Typical of late twentieth century refineries, Fawley is home-based, capital intensive (i.e. a lot of apparatus and machinery in proportion to men) and technically very sophisticated. Also it is in the South, far away from the old coal-bearing regions which were once the basis of British fuel, power and industry. Here imported crude oil is 'cracked' into petrol and other fuels.

23 *Above* An oil tanker: the SS *Ashtabula* (1901) shows the essential tanker design, unchanged to this day: engines and accommodation aft to minimise fire risk. This vessel was of 4,527 tons, compared with 500,000-tonners of the 1970's, but was, just the same, a vital link in transporting this primary fuel from source to generator.

24 *Below* An Oil Terminal: vehicles and staff on parade at Hammersmith Bulk plant to celebrate the arrival of A 8182, the Anglo-American Oil Co's first tanker, perhaps Britain's first road tanker lorry (1905). It delivered lamp oil under evocative brand names like Tea Rose, White Rose and Royal Daylight, once household words. A-A is now the familiar Esso. Note foreman in traditional bowler hat.

orthodox means, like trains or lorries. Also it can be sent by pipeline, thereby adding another power grid to the networks that serve Great Britain, like gas or electricity. The first such pipelines were built by the state in wartime to supply RAF airfields, but after the war an ambitious programme started in 1951 to pump large quantities of crude oil by pipe, from terminals to refineries. Two such pipelines are the Central Scotland pipeline, fifty-seven miles long and the sixty-mile-long Milford Haven–Llandarcy pipeline. Pipes to carry finished products like aviation spirit, ethylene, gas oil, etc., were constructed from 1960, and they include the 140-mile line from Stanlow near Manchester to Avonmouth, and the Fawley–Severnside line (seventy-eight miles); the longest to date is the *UK Oil Pipeline Project* of 1963 (Thames–Mersey, 245 miles).

Oil and the State

The gas, coal and electricity industries have been moulded by repeated and often vigorous legislation for much of their existences. Oil legislation exists, too, but because oil was never a 'public utility' and because the major problem of extraction lay abroad, oil statutes have been fewer and rather different to the normal power-laws. The main connection between oil and the state has been the desire of various governments to tax the fuel (see p. 24) from 1909 onwards. At first this was simply to raise revenue, and the tax was 3d (1½p) per gallon of motor spirit. In later years the tax was adjusted to protect coal (or reduce dependence on imported fuel), and a duty of 2d (1p) per gallon was put on fuel oil in 1961, which deliberately made oil more expensive than coal – in fact it was said to subsidise the latter to the tune of £1 3s 0d (£1.15) per ton! The state imposes taxes on all kinds of commodities and transactions so that it may share in general prosperity, and as there is never any shortage of calls upon its funds, it is always anxious to widen its 'tax base'. Preferably it taxes things for which there is inelastic (i.e. sustained, relatively rigid) demand, so it is a clear mark of Britain's increasing dependence on oil that oil taxes have been repeatedly raised from 3d (1½p) per gallon in 1909 to 3s 7d (18p) per gallon in 1967. In 1933 the government noted that more vehicles were using 'derv' (diesel engined road vehicle) fuel, so it imposed a tax of 1d (½p) per gallon on it; from 1935 the rate was put up to that of normal fuel. Since coal has not been taxed from the 1830s, and neither gas nor electricity have ever been taxed (and it would probably raise a political typhoon if it were suggested!) oil remains uniquely the one source of power to be taxed in modern times.

There are other connections between the state and the oil industry, for example the Petroleum Act (1934) which nationalised all oil and natural gas under British soil (cf. coal royalties, 1938) – a matter of great importance thirty years later when such resources were found. The Pipeline Act (1962) required government agreement for all large pipeline schemes since they were a major invasion of the environment and, like early gas schemes, needed to burrow under plenty of property. For strategic reasons the Petroleum Board (1939–48) assumed overall control of the industry during and after the Second World War. By further government fiat petrol was rationed (1939–50) and marketed for most of that period (and until 1953), as a single brand, 'Pool', whose grey-and-white tankers and pumps were symbols of wartime and the 'age of austerity' which followed it.

As coal was once a major export, so oil is now a major import, the largest single one by value; in 1968 Britain imported eighty-one million tons of crude oil (£627 million worth), although petro-chemicals exported from Britain offset this by £150 million. The many uses of oil and the many aspects of social and economic life dependent on it (e.g. plastics and central heating) have placed it in a very strong position. It is not 'King Oil', however, as coal was once primary fuel monarch, for it has to share the fuel market with other suppliers. The balance among these fuels is a vital matter to governments, and has resulted in various official fuel policies, dealt with later (Chapter 7).

There are other broader considerations relating to oil. First the purchase of oil from overseas has intensified the 'international economy' which has become a feature of civilisation in the last two centuries. The large oil companies are international in outlook, and are an important strand in the 'global net' of trade. Secondly, oil has often been found in relatively poor countries, which therefore benefit. Supplying oil has become a lucrative business for such countries as Kuwait and Venezuela. Thirdly (and connected) these funds flowing to poor countries are often returned to buy manufactured goods from the industrial West, which therefore benefits by having to purchase oil abroad, in the way that British demand for Argentine meat in the nineteenth century helped that country to buy British manufactured goods.

Finally, and long term, oil will not last for ever; like coal it is a 'once only' fossil fuel. It has perpetuated a certain type of civilisation, but in spite of appearances there is no lasting equilibrium in economies or societies. Abundant oil reserves do exist (only five per cent of possible oil-bearing regions have been surveyed as yet), yet one day it is certain that it will become scarce and expensive and uncompetitive. It is for such reasons that research goes on into alternative sources of power, like nuclear or solar power. Careful prophets bear in mind our absolute dependence on power, and the essential mortality of most primary fuels.

FURTHER READING
C. Tughendat, *Oil, The Biggest Business*, is a sound historical survey. See also P. H. Giddens, *The Birth of the Oil Industry* (1938).

5 Gas

Although the public supply of water has been common for centuries, and whole civilisations (e.g. Mesopotamia and Egypt) depended on it, the gas industry is really the first public utility of modern times. This is because from its birth it showed some distinctly modern tendencies: it depended upon sophisticated technology, required large amounts of capital to launch it and had a peculiar relationship with the state which both protected and inspected it so that it might serve the public better.

Usually the 'gas' spoken of in these terms is Town Gas – the gas supplied to homes and industry and obtained by gasifying coal or oil. Recently, since 1966, Britain has been able to employ Natural Gas from below the bed of the North Sea. By 1975 this natural gas will account for most gas distributed in Britain, and coal gas will be a fading memory. In addition to these familiar gases there are and have been various industrial gases: producer gas, Dowson gas, etc., all of which have been valuable sources of industrial energy. For convenience, also, there have been portable gases, such as calor gas (**56**), and these can have wide domestic and industrial application too. Town gas has always had the lion's share of the total gas market, and it dominates the history of gas as a source of power.

As with oil and electricity, gas was first employed as a source of light. Its long reign as a source of heat and industrial power came much later, indeed until 1920 the quality of gas was officially measured by its illuminating power. Today we measure its quality in the therm (from the Greek *thermos*: hot), not in the candle-power, that so many cubic feet of gas will give.

Technical History

For most of its history, town gas was generated by heating coal, hence its alternative title 'coal-gas'. As so often there is no arbitrary 'first' inventor, but for convenience credit is given to William Murdoch, who made coal-gas between 1792 and 1802. There are records of it before this: a Dr Clayton, Dean of Kildare (1691), is recorded as having filled a bladder with coal-gas and then burst it before his audience, showing how the escaping gas caused a light to burn brighter – fortunately his crude distillation plant made a weak gas, or the experiments would have had another and sadly dramatic end! Other experimenters knew that distilled coal gave off an inflammable gas: Lord Dundonald lit the hall of Culross Abbey this way (1782).

William Murdoch, however, was more thorough and systematic, and timed his discovery well. He was a talented engineer, and lit his house at Redruth, Cornwall, by coal-gas in 1792. Ten years later he lit the whole factory of his employer, James Watt, at Soho, Birmingham, with an enlarged coal-gas plant.

By 1804 the Soho system was sufficiently perfected for the firm to offer to erect plant elsewhere for the manufacture and distribution of coal-gas. Some shrewd businessmen of the day were attracted by the offer: it might enable them to keep their factories working at night in a more satisfactory way than relying on dim oil lamps and candles. Small factory gas plants were erected for the cotton mills of Messrs Phillips and Lee (1805), Messrs Kennedy, and Messrs Burleigh, all of Manchester. By using 150 tons of coal per year the first named of these sustained a constant 2,500 candle-power light.

One of Murdoch's protégés, Samuel Clegg, struck out on his own and propagated the 'new light' by setting up small gasworks in factories and other establishments – even in an enterprising school (Stonyhurst, 1811). In 1806 he suggested that Manchester employed gas for street lighting, but the offer was premature. On the other hand, the engineer Josiah Pemberton, in selling a gas plant to the Golden Lane Brewery, London, persuaded his client to run a few nearby street lights off the system, thus pioneering the modern networks of street and highway

25 A Gas City: part of the giant Beckton Gasworks of the old Gas Light and Coke Co., purpose-built to receive sea coal in 1870. On the left is the water gas plant, on the right the batteries of coke ovens (1932). One of the 4 million cu. ft. gasholders (there were 7 once) lurks in the background of this power factory which could generate 33,000 million cu. ft. of gas (1956) and use 1¾ million tons of coal p.a. It supplied much of East and North East London.

26 Beckton within: gas workers servicing the retorts where the coal was baked into gas; for 150 years the gas industry used these arduous methods, full of din and thick vapours like a vision out of *Paradise Lost*. Later, oil and natural gas modernised this industry and made it capital-intensive. 12 or 18 hour shifts in these conditions were common until the 1870's. Note sweat rags hanging from workers' clothing.

illumination. Next year gas street-lighting got far greater publicity when London's fashionable Pall Mall was lit by gas. For many years thereafter gas lighting was all the rage for go-ahead towns; it became a symbol of improvement as tramways and electricity were to become later.

By 1812 there were probably twenty gas plants working successfully, and some London businessmen felt sufficiently confident to found the Chartered Gas Light and Coke Co. to supply any type of customers from a central gas works. Their enterprise was significantly named: coke is the baked coal remaining after gasification, and was (until the 1960s) an important by-product of gasmaking. It had a large market as a smokeless fuel; tar was another commercially important by-product. If the coal is lightly baked (heated below 600°C) it is said to have undergone low-temperature carbonisation. This was popular and normal with early gasworks, because it yielded a rich gas which gave off a good light, as well as plenty of easily ignitable coke. Later, when gas became popular for heating and cooking, and for valuable by-products which could be released by great heating, up to 1,000°C, the industry used high-temperature carbonisation.

The other factor enshrined in the company's name was its legal status: 'chartered'. Gas supply is a special type of economic enterprise. It does not lend itself to vigorous competition in a given area, like the selling of baked beans or dry cleaning. Obviously householders do not want multitudes of gas pipes from rival companies disfiguring their houses. Gas companies wanted, and tended to get, local monopolies and these could only be guaranteed by public authority, by statute, i.e. legally binding documents issued by the state, usually by an Act of Parliament. Other factors suggested this course of action, for instance the need of gas companies to dig up the public highway in order to lay and maintain gas mains – the network of iron pipes which distributed the new form of power.

It is important to note the close interlocking of people and processes in the industrial revolution. Murdoch worked for Watt, whose mechanical 'know-how' and business connections enabled him to spread the gas system quickly. Enterprising manufacturers did not have qualms about giving the system a try, and most early plants were in Northern industrial towns. In turn, the gas industry stimulated the demand for coal and iron, and created a new market for cheap, smokeless coke, and other by-products.

The Gas Light and Coke Co. lasted until nationalisation in 1949, and its success soon inspired other towns and cities to follow. A less successful rival, the London Portable Gas Co. (1819–34), tried to supply customers with the new fuel in copper cylinders of two cubic feet each, thus avoiding the need for mains; but the idea was too far ahead of its time. Another variation was oil gas (1815) which gave an even richer fuel than coal and was launched by its sanguine inventor as 'inflammable air or olefiant gas applicable to the purpose of giving light'. Unfortunately the high cost of oil stunted the growth of this process which was generally employed by those who had access to cheap waste-oil, like railway companies. It was favoured for railway-carriage lighting.

Coal-gas entered on its long supremacy with no serious rivals in sight. It was generated in retorts, or closed baking chambers. These were laboriously hand-fired by three-man gangs of stokers who would wield 9-foot-long scoops containing up to $1\frac{1}{2}$ cwt. of coal for each 'charge'. Mechanical stoking was more convenient and speedy and came in the 1870s. The lofty retort houses were, with the massive gasholders, a familiar part of the urban scene. Wherever industry wanted coke, especially in steel-producing areas, it erected coke-ovens. These regarded the coal gas which they produced as a by-product, but often sold it to nearby gas undertakings to ease their supply problem, thereby integrating further the industrial pattern.

Behind the gradual development of improved retorts, by-product manufacture, etc., lay the root problem of all power industries: how to get 'more with less' – more power with fewer men or quantities of capital employed per therm or horsepower produced. This single problem was the force behind the myriads of technical changes which took place in the nineteenth and twentieth centuries, and which culminated in the most efficient gasification process of all, the Lurgi process (1962). Lurgi generators were a fraction of the size of old coal gas works, but exceeded their ancestors in output. Already the use of natural gas has rendered even the technical perfection of the 1960s obsolescent. Improved efficiency was measured by noting how much gas could be produced per given weight of coal. For example, from 1920 to 1939 it was calculated that had there been no technical improvement the gas industry would have been using an extra $3\frac{1}{2}$ million tons of coal per year by 1940, a very considerable saving.

The storage of power is nearly always difficult, and it may be impossible as with AC electric current, or highly dangerous as with petrol. Gas, however, may be stored in immense quantities safely and cheaply and so can await peak demand without fear of cuts in supply. Gasholders (or 'gasometers') are of three types. The first was the 'bell' floating on water (1782) which is now obsolete, then came the still-familiar 'telescopic' pattern (1826) and finally the fixed tower (1925). Early holders contained about 15,000 cu. ft of gas (1817), by 1874 there was a holder of five million cu. ft, and by 1900, twelve million cu. ft. As already men-

27 Power for power: a worker tends one of the simple and elegant steam-driven gas compressors at the Mond Gasworks, Dudley Port (see **28**). Built in 1905, these engines worked until 1963.

tioned, these holders, with the nearby retorts, puffs of steam and singular smells wafting around the works' environs became marked and familiar parts of the Victorian scene; the use of natural gas will sweep them away, apart from the storage holders.

The Changing Use of Gas: Less Light, More Heat
From the gas works the fuel was pumped along mains which served the most populous areas of Britain; long-distance distribution was rare until modern times, so each town had its local gasworks and sometimes more than one. Until about 1890 gas was used as a lighting agent, and demand schedules show this (**30**). Today gas is used for cooking and heating, and the changeover came towards the turn of the century. Because gas light was so important, the industry reflected the fact: low-temperature carbonisation was the rule since it gave up to 18 candle-

49

28 and **29**   The gas revolution: *Above* The former works of the South Staffs. Mond Gas Co. at Dudley Port, Staffs: here coal conveyers hoisted 40 tons of coal per hour (by hopper chains) and dropped it into producers (1901). *Below* On the same site has arisen the modern Tipton oil-gas works (1964), cleaner and more capital-intensive.

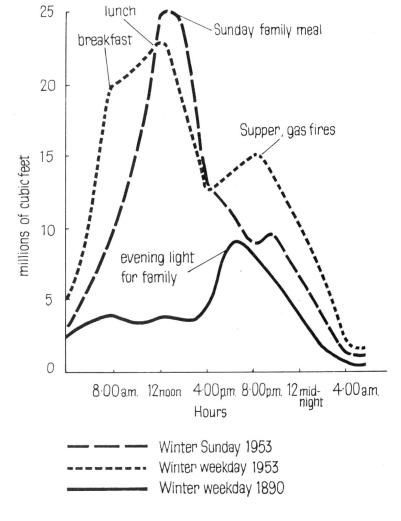

30 The changing demand for gas as shown on a typical Winter day (1890) when it was used for lighting, to a similar day in 1953 when it was used for heating.

millions of cubic feet

lunch
breakfast
Sunday family meal
Supper, gas fires
evening light for family

8.00 a.m. 12 noon 4.00 pm. 8.00 pm. 12 mid-night 4.00 a.m.
Hours

— — — Winter Sunday 1953
▪▪▪▪▪▪▪▪ Winter weekday 1953
━━━━━ Winter weekday 1890

power in the normal argand burner, and Scottish or Lancashire cannel coal (p. 22) was preferred because it gave up to 28 candle-power; benzole vapour and naphthalene were introduced into the gas to enrich it further.

Two factors changed this pattern. First the incandescent mantle was introduced for lighting (1890–1905); this was a cap of thorium gauze which glowed brilliantly when heated, therefore hot gas, not bright gas, became a more important consideration, and engineers devised processes accordingly. The other factor was the coming of electric light (p. 58) which, for those who might afford it, was altogether superior, being clean, odourless and potentially brighter. The shareholders of gas companies were gloomy at the spread of electric lighting. Technical and social changes soon changed their attitude. First, gas cooking developed. Very primitive gas cookers had been used by individualist chefs, for instance by Charles Soyer at the Reform Club in 1841, but the true domestic cooker dates from 1851. At first gas undertakings were not much interested in this new use for their product: they preferred to let pressure fall during the daytime between the (then) peaks of demand. The more commercially-minded gas-makers began hiring out cookers to interested users from the 1870s rightly guessing

51

that continuous and steady demand for gas was to their advantage. Gas stoves improved quickly in design, they were easier to clean when they were enamelled (1913), and easier to control when managed by a 'Regulo' thermostat (1923). Other gas heaters were the modern gas fire (1882); the gas geyser for heating water (1868) and for heating it instantaneously as it flowed (1890) – the famous 'Ascot' dates from 1932.

The most revolutionary social change to affect the gas industry during its first renaissance (c. 1890–1910) was the penny-in-the-slot meter (1889), by which poorer customers could pay for gas as they used it. The prepayment meter suited people of slender means and little credit, and also gas suppliers who could now tap bigger markets. Gas power could be enjoyed, by 1900, by rich and poor alike and was a true 'public utility'. Furthermore, it became cheaper: it had cost 75p per 1,000 cu. ft in 1824, but only 12½p per 1,000 cu. ft in 1900.

Industry increasingly used gas as a source of power; the gas engine (1866) from which all modern internal combustion engines are descended, became a popular source of industrial energy up to the First World War, and the use of gas in metal working and general boiling was common after 1880. Industrial users included the Royal Mint, Woolwich Arsenal and hundreds of small factories and workshops in, for example, the Black Country and Sheffield, where metal-working was common. In recent years the industrial use of gas has become commonplace, accounting for nearly one-third of all gas sales by 1958. Its slow

31 Natural Gas: the Gas Council-Amoco drilling rig *Orion*, flaring off natural gas from under the North Sea in its early days (1967) before connection to the gas grid; a dramatic and attractive example of improved technology enabling engineers to tap new sources of power. Uniquely, gas has moved from a secondary to a primary fuel industry (page 6).

adoption in the century before 1914 was mainly owing to the cheap and abundant supply of coal; gas has become more popular because of its favourable comparative cost. In 1967 gas supplied six per cent of all energy requirements, and by 1980 after the second gas renaissance (occasioned by natural gas) it may be twenty per cent.

Industrial Gases

Not all gas came from gasworks; coke-oven suppliers have already been noted; even in 1957 at the end of the coal-gas era some fourteen per cent of gas came this way. Industry used and generated other gases for power, as well as coal gas. Steel mills tapped blast-furnace gases and used them to drive gas engines which kept up the blast for the furnaces – a neat example of fuel economy which came after the fuel-and-power conscious B. H. Thwaite (**55**) demonstrated its feasibility (1895). He had lamented the waste of gas worth $\frac{3}{4}$ million h.p. per day, which had previously gone to light up the night skies of Merthyr or Barrow.

The more orthodox industrial gases were especially generated as such, and were obtained by gasifying various fuels in retorts called 'producers' which made producer (or Siemens) gas, water gas or semi-water (Dowson) gas. These gases had a variety of uses; Dowson gas drove many of the rugged gas engines that powered industry between the steam and electric eras, and Siemens gas was a cheap source of heat. Industrial gases were simple to make, and made a factory independent of the town gas system. Their main appeal was cheapness and convenience in an age when electricity was uncommon and highly expensive.

One undertaking, the South Staffordshire Mond Gas Co. (1901) actually set up a central industrial gas station at Tipton, Staffs to supply 120 square miles of industrial England with industrial gas. It was not copied, although the plant survived until 1963. Modern industrial gases derived from refined oil are Propane and Butane, but these are delivered to factories by tanker rather than generated on the premises. A portable gas favoured by homes and factories removed from mains supplies (and by campers and caravanners) is Calor Gas (1935). The early advertising of the firm which made it hints at the primitive conditions which were still common at the time: 'Do you want gas? You are miles from a gas main and can imagine no alternative to the everlasting pricking of burners, trimming of wicks, filling up of reservoirs (refers to oil lamps), laborious carting of coal, removal of ashes, dust and soot. . . .'

Natural Gas

In the early 1960s it seemed as if oil-gas was going to take over from coal-gas as the main town gas. This phase proved to be short-lived, following the discovery of large reserves of natural gas under the North Sea. Natural gas was already known elsewhere, it had been used very locally in ancient China, and for the first time in the industrial era at Fedonia, New York (USA) in 1824 where a simple wooden grid distributed it. In Britain, Heathfield in Sussex had a small network from the turn of the century. Heathfield railway station, hotel and a few houses benefited from this small field.

The big North European field was found in the Dutch province of Groningen (1959). An intensive search went on to see if there was natural gas nearer to Britain, while the gas was actually imported as a frozen liquid (from Algeria) from 1964, and fed into normal gas mains. Following the 1965 discovery it has been possible to plan a national high-pressure gas grid which should reach most parts of Britain by 1980. This will effect a complete revolution in the industry – local works will close (and have already started to do so) as generation becomes unnecessary. Ever since nationalisation (1949) regional grids had concentrated gas production on larger stations, and small ones had been closing. Within a decade from 1970 the 'local gasworks' will have gone from the urban scene. The change also increases the potency of the whole British economy and industrial structure (cf. Thwaite, p. 5) because natural gas is indigenous and already 'generated by nature' as coal was in the past.

The Industrial Structure of Gas

The generation and distribution of gas grew in an *ad hoc* manner, unplanned and piecemeal as towns or villages decided to take advantage of the convenience and delights of coal-gas. Sometimes a large house or factory made its own gas, more usually a local gas undertaking supplied it from a central works to anybody willing to purchase it. This pattern remained until 1949 when the whole industry was vested in twelve 'Area Boards', which received some guidance from a central Gas Council.

When public supply of gas started (1810–40) local government was not organised for such a business, and private companies usually composed of public-spirited local shareholders, performed the task of laying on gas. Most towns were then subject to the inert oligarchies which lasted until the Municipal Corporations Act of 1835, and such bodies showed no interest in building gas-works, although progressive Manchester's 'Police Commissioners' did build a gasworks as early as 1817 (note: 'police' was used here in its original sense derived from the Greek *polis*, a city – it meant general supervision of the whole town, not just law and order).

Gas companies were of two types. Statutory Companies were set up by a private Act of Parliament which gave them a legal monopoly, permission to dig up streets and fix charges, occasionally in return for controlled profits to prevent the exploitation of consumers. Local monopoly was not formally granted until 1860. There were also Non-Statutory Companies which relied upon local goodwill to perform their task, and which tended, therefore, to serve small and less complicated communities. By 1920 there were over 1,300 gas undertakings of which 780 were statutory and did most of the gas generation. After 1875 local government was allowed to purchase gas companies. By then it was entering on something of a golden age of municipal enterprise, and gladly assumed such

32 Rochdale Gas Works generating gas for a self-contained municipal system in one of the famous Lancashire cotton towns. The system was nationalised in 1949. Originally built by a private company in 1824, it was bought by the Corporation 20 years later.

responsibilities as the generation of gas or electricity. Some 300 companies were 'municipalised', mostly North of the Trent, and especially in Lancashire where Blackpool, Lancaster, Accrington, Oldham and Rochdale were among the corporations that ran gasworks.

Gas companies ranged widely in size, from the mammoth Gas Light and Coke Co. which supplied most of North London ($1\frac{1}{2}$ million consumers, thirteen gasworks) to small local concerns like the Langport, Huish and Currey Rivel Gas Co. in rural Somerset (340 consumers, one gasworks). In later years there was some amalgamation of gas undertakings and the construction of local grids. In common with most public utilities, gas was nationalised; by the Gas Act of 1949 the state bought the industry for £227 million. At first its organisation reflected the technical fact of local generation and distribution, but after the natural gas era started the central Gas Council was given wide powers of planning and manufacture (Gas Act, 1965), a good example of administrative change reflecting technical progress. A 'case history' to illustrate these changes is that of the Tunbridge Wells Gas Co., set up in 1843 (non-statutory) and receiving a charter (therefore statutory) in 1864. In 1929 it took over the Crowborough Gas

55

Co., and in 1945 the Wadhurst Gas Co. In 1949 it was vested in the South Eastern Gas Board and in 1967 its works were shut and dismantled as the area was by then connected to the national grid. Only the gasholders remain as evidence of former enterprise. Most areas of Great Britain can supply similar microcosm histories, and they are interesting to investigate.

Gas and Society

By 1850 most large towns had gas lighting. The dangers of dark or dimly-lit streets lessened, thus the Gas Light and Coke Co.'s 1812 prospectus castigated contemporary street lighting as being 'not only dismal, but hardly (enabling) the passenger to distinguish the watchman from the thief, or the pavement from the gutter'. Now they would supply a light 'little inferior to daylight' and banish gloom 'formerly borne because . . . inevitable'. It would be tedious to list all the many appliances which followed gas lamps as agents of social change: ovens, geysers, irons, refrigerators, fires, etc. — there was even a proposed gas radio! Many have been described already, and they have all shaped new, convenient and comfortable ways of life for nearly 200 years.

A large and valuable by-product industry grew out of gas manufacture, and prior to the making of gas, many miners were involved in cutting the coal fuel for it: 230,000 in 1939. Certain coalfields were particularly favoured by the gas industry, notably the North-East coast which continued the old 'sea coal' tradition by sending the fuel by sea to the South, and notably to the Thames-side gas works like Beckton and Brentford.

Important public utilities, like gas, have called the state into action and given it further scope as the protector and inspector of the public interest. In this way the state continued its traditional paternal rôle right through the so-called age of free enterprise in the nineteenth century. The main gas laws are listed below:

1812 Gas Light and Coke Co. Act: the first statutory gas company
1820–50 Many company acts passed
1847 Gas Works Clauses Act: codifies previous orders and laws
1860 Metropolis Gas Companies Act: mainly affects London and testing of gas by inspectors for purity
1871 Gas Works Clauses Act: extends 'London testing' everywhere
1875 Public Health Act: allows municipalisation of gas companies
1920 Gas Regulation Act: future standard of measurement by heating, not lighting capacity
1949 Gas Act: nationalised industry
1964 Continental Shelf Act: stakes out North Sea natural gas areas
1965 Gas Act: makes Gas Council the key organisation of the industry now that local generation is doomed. Similarly, 1971, proposal to have one Gas Corporation for England.

Some significant historical statistics relating to the gas industry are as follows:

Growth of Consumers
1920:   7½ million
1939:   11 million
1957–69: 13 million

Although no change is recorded in the last two dates, it must be noted that each consumer buys more gas as a rule: 1967–69 gas sales rose by 10 per cent.

Coal used to generate gas
1815: *c.* 55,000 tons
1939; 19 million tons
1957: 34 million tons (81 per cent gas from coal)
1969: 11 million tons (13 per cent gas from coal)
1975: (forecast) no coal, little oil, virtually all natural gas.

Gasworks, total number	*Output of gas* (millions of cu. ft per year)
1820: 15	1815: 250
1830: 200	1882: 65,000
1949: 1,050	1920: 230,000
1957: 600	1939: 342,000
1970: 170	1949: 482,000
	1957: 550,000
	1969: 1,028,212
	1975: (est.) 3,000 per day

By 1970 there were thirty million gas appliances of all kinds in Great Britain. An important social factor is that the gas industry has been able to enjoy an increasing proportion of people's spending in the age of the so-called 'affluent society'. The old saying has it: 'one generation's luxuries are the next's necessities'. Thus gas fires and stoves are accepted as a matter of course now, and central heating is showing signs of becoming such. There is a further meaning: as people have more spending power they take up such luxuries as gaslight (if they are Victorians) or central heating (today), while their spending on food stays much the same, or increases sluggishly. All power industries benefit from this tendency. Finally, it is interesting to note that the gas industry, really the doyen of public utilities, has been 'saved' twice. It staved off the threat of electric lighting by concentrating on heating, and it neutralised the threat of ever-increasing coal prices by employing first, oil and latterly natural gas. The Jeremiads of many experts and observers were unfounded, and gas will enter its second century as a flourishing public service.

FURTHER READING
Although quite a number of books, or sections of them, describe the various (now obsolescent) methods of gas generation, it is remarkable that so key an industry has no good history. However, a most excellent and informative technical history does exist: *Town Gas – Its Manufacture and Distribution* by E. G. Stewart (HMSO).

6 Electricity

To many people electricity is synonymous with power. If a house has 'power laid on' it refers to electricity supply. Electric power is only one kind, and it is the youngest of the 'secondary fuels', but its growth has been so vast and its effects so revolutionary that it can well claim to be the premier power industry. There are good reasons for describing its development after that of gas. Electric power came late in the industrial society (about 1880 onwards) and had to fight vigorously in the face of well-entrenched coal and gas power sources. From its birth the electricity industry has been most closely watched and directed by the state. At first the effects of this were little short of disastrous, but they became beneficial to society and the industry when the initial mistakes were rectified.

Technical History

The origins of the industry are quite simple, and can be fairly ascribed to one master-mind, Michael Faraday. In the late autumn of 1831 Faraday discovered, within a few months, the essential principle of the dynamo (which generates direct current, DC), the alternator (alternating current, AC) and the transformer which can step voltages up or down – an essential matter in the long distance transmission of electric power, and a necessity to a modern industrial society. Other men have developed machinery based on these principles, and Faraday himself had a path beaten before him by pioneers like Volta and Galvani, or Oersted, who discovered the relationship between magnetism and electricity (1820).

Soon after Faraday's *annus mirabilis* an electric motor was produced, but it took many years to develop reliable or efficient electrical machinery, and so there was an hiatus of some fifty years between Faraday's work and a really promising or viable electric power industry. Occasionally during the interim, clear progress was made as science or technology perfected one more process; thus a crude but rugged 2-ton dynamo was constructed to generate current for the arc lamps of the South Foreland lighthouse (1858), the first public adoption of electric lighting. After the appearance of Gramme's improved dynamo (1870) the 'electric age' was properly launched, because Gramme's machine was really reliable and it 'opened up a new age in electrical engineering: the electric current was no longer experimental but could be made available on a practical scale'. (P. Dunsheath.)

As with gas and oil, electricity was originally seen mainly as a source of lighting. When, therefore, a clean and convenient electric lamp was invented by Swan and Edison (1878–1879) a sustained demand for the new power began to develop. Hitherto the brilliant but short-lived arc lamp, as used at the South Foreland

33 The Electric light: one of the world's first electric lights, an early 'Swan' from his factory at South Benwell, near Newcastle Upon Tyne. It is mounted in a converted gas light, and works by electrically heating a carbon filament in a vacuum. Later bulbs had different shapes and filaments, but the principle remained.

light, was the only known way of using electric power for lighting. Once again a marked development in technology accelerated a whole industry. The first private house to use Swan's lamp was his own, closely followed by Armstrong's (p. 15) in 1880. In 1881 the Savoy Theatre, then in its great years as the home of the Gilbert and Sullivan operettas, was the first public place to use the new electric lamps – it employed 1,200 of them with 100 blue-tinted ones to 'give effect to night scenes'. Other early users of the electric light demonstrated its versatility and by their nature hinted at its probable future: W. D. & H. O. Wills' tobacco factory, the British Museum reading room, Avonmouth Docks and the 'fronts' of Brighton, Eastbourne and Hastings.

Since those early days electricity has also revolutionised other aspects of society and industry. It has played a vital part in the conquest of distance which separates communities from each other, and from essential resources. Electricity came too late to power the railway revolution in its most effective age, but it did develop urban transport by means of electric 'traction' – the word generally applied to electrically-powered transport.

The first electric vehicle was probably Robert Davidson's railcar (1840), but it and all similar 'primitives' were too crude and slow to be a practical solution to the problem of locomotion. Improved dynamos and motors, together with wire or rail conducted current (thus dispensing with heavy batteries) came into existence

59

34 Powered Telecommunications: an operator at the pioneer Marconi transatlantic wireless station, Clifden, Co. Galway, (1905). The Clifden station started commercial service in 1908 and shut in 1922; it generated its own power by peat and coal; interestingly, the first transatlantic flight landed here in 1919.

from the 1880s onwards, the first such systems in the British Isles being the Giant's Causeway Tramway (see p. 15) and Volk's Railway at Brighton in 1883. Urban electric tramways, usually operating on a voltage of 500–600 volts DC were to be found in most heavily populated parts of Britain from 1890–1940. Electric trams increased the pace of urban life, and extended it by creating more accessible suburbs. Electric trains, on existing or occasionally new railways, had even more marked effects because they created outer suburbs and 'dormitory towns' from which people could travel up to work each day; the towns of Orpington, Malden, Rickmansworth and Barnet, all round London, are largely creations of the electric traction era.

Electric motors have virtually numberless applications elsewhere: in industry alone they work machine-tools, hoists, lathes, drills, etc. Electric power for industry was pioneered in the North-East coast heavy engineering area, where Neptune Bank power station (1901) supplied some of the leading shipyards and engineering works near Wallsend. Since then most factories have adopted electric power, and incidentally freed themselves from miles of dangerous and less efficient belt transmission of power (from central steam or motor engines) which used to add considerably to industrial accidents. Electric power is amenable to various types of automatic and remote control, and makes completely automated factories possible. Similarly the electronic computer has replaced tedious mental tasks which were previously mastered slowly, or not at all.

Computers have completely altered much of what is loosely called 'communications' – the collation and dissemination of facts and data. Telecommunications, that is communications over a long distance (implicitly aided by electric power), date from the earliest days of electricity. Cooke and Wheatstone demonstrated a practical electric telegraph in 1837, by sending messages over two miles. By 1870 there were 16,000 miles of electric telegraph line. Other important electric-based telecommunications were the telephone (1875), the wireless telegraph (1896) and television (1927) – it is obvious how much society depends on these communications media today.

35 *Above* The BBC medium and short wave station at Daventry, Northants (1932); because of its strategic importance it had its own power plant.

36 *Below* Inside Daventry: part of the modulator stages, a far cry from the early Clifden sets, twenty-seven years before.

37 Selection of bulbs: from the mid-1920's. Profits from lamp sales (organised through a pricing-ring: a manufacturers' agreement not to compete on prices) were a major prop for British electrical engineers in the lean inter-war years. *Osram* was the GEC brand name; *Metrovick* was a branch of AEI (now GEC also). Note the price: 1/– (worth 4/– or 5/– 25p today) one item in the cost of living index which has fallen over the years!

At home, electricity has often been said to have 'emancipated the housewife', a phrase frequently used by those who are strangers to household chores. However, if housewives are not free of work, their task is certainly simpler if they can use vacuum cleaners or washing machines; the former were quite common before 1940, the latter are mainly a development of the 1950s. To produce this large array of electrical equipment, both domestic and industrial, there has grown up a large electrical engineering industry: in 1924 there were 173,000 employees in electrical engineering; in 1939, 367,000, and by 1970 the figure had risen to 910,000.

Before 1914, a mixture of caution and complacency among investors left much of the field in electrical engineering open to foreign firms, or their British subsidiaries. In this way Britain got a taste of foreign ownership, having hitherto been an owner of overseas railways, electricity works, etc. These new firms were, for example, Siemens (German); British Westinghouse and British

Thomson-Houston (USA). Many of these firms later became British-owned, and many amalgamated. Between the World Wars (1919–1939) electrical engineering was one of the new or 'science-based' industries that took up the slack left by the declining old staples like cotton and shipbuilding. This industry serves as a microcosm in demonstrating three strong trends of modern industry: its international character; its technological basis, and its tendency to amalgamate into giants, like GEC-AEI. This industry, and power generation itself have become not only typical, but dominant and all-pervading. Truly, it has become what the American man of letters, Henry Adams, said it would: 'The Age of the Dynamo' – to him the power generator had replaced gothic cathedrals as the symbol of the force and basis of a whole civilisation.

38 Power applied: in the home. The Vacuum cleaner (1907) is a familiar piece of domestic machinery now, here are the 1926 models and sundry gadgetry of the same year, novelties at the time but familiar now, another example of 'one generation's luxuries are the next's necessities'.

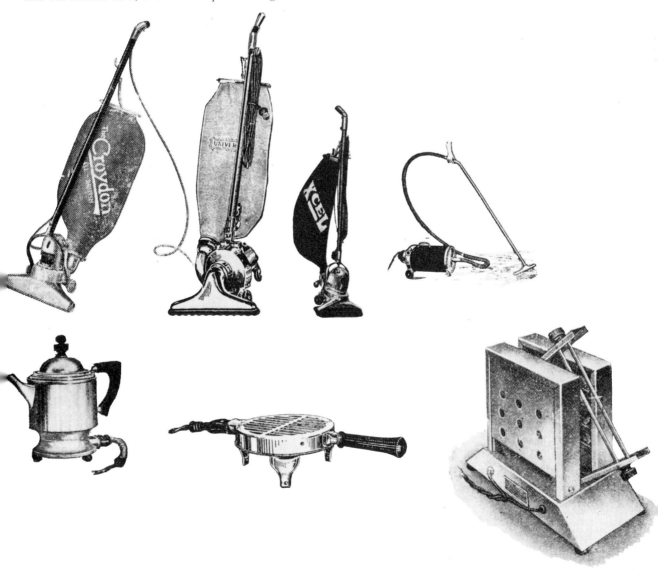

39 Electrical Engineering: the power industry both needs its own machinery, and stimulates demand for it in order to exploit 'secondary fuels'—in this case electricity. Here at a Bolton works (1890) part of a 10,000 hp alternator is being assembled for Ferranti's revolutionary station at Deptford.

Electricity Supply

The flowering of technology which had brought the use of electricity so far by 1914 was unfortunately not matched by similar intelligence in organising its supply. Matters came to such a pass that suppliers of electrical equipment for a modern industrial state had to contend with 642 separate supply undertakings of which 282 supplied AC only, 283 AC and DC and seventy-seven DC only – there were, moreover, forty-three different voltages! (1934).

The gap between the enthusiastic competence of engineers and the 'parish pump' organisation of supply was largely the result of badly-framed laws, and the skilful delaying tactics of various private and municipal interests who obstructed any tendency to a national system of electricity supply. They had a certain quixotic pride in their undertakings, but noble though this might be, it did damage the interests of the community at large. London suffered the saddest muddle of all, with its kaleidoscopic variety of undertakings and standards (seventy suppliers, twenty-four voltages and ten frequencies in 1918) and where the boroughs of Islington and St Pancras dismissed the idea of linking their systems as 'an illusion' (1914). Although the far-seeing engineer S. Z. de Ferranti postulated (and started to build) a central generating station for London in 1888, in practice most of the patchwork survived until 1948.

One should not contrast too strongly, however, the 'sensible' engineers with the 'devious' politicians. The political muddle was not helped by a furious professional war among electrical engineers at the turn of the century as to the relative merits of AC and DC. It was like the 'battle of the gauges' which had plagued the railways in their youth, before men realised that a national network was coming. Many people failed to see that long-distance transmission of power would be normal one day (AC is superior for this) and that the difficulties of AC supply could be overcome. Direct current fought a long battle and eventually lost: by 1970 only 400 out of Britain's near-eighteen million electricity consumers used it. Another battle, relating only to the AC camp, was over frequency: eventually this was fixed at 50 Hz, but by that time so many appliances were built to take other frequencies that the change cost £17½ million (1930).

The root of this chaos lay in the Electric Lighting Acts of 1882 and 1888. The only solution was nationalisation (1948). In between these statutes lay a long period of confusion and ineffectual compromise. Acts of Parliament usually reflect fashionable economic and political dogmas of the day. The 1882 Act recognised (i) private enterprise as a suitable means of supplying power, but (ii) contemporary horror of private monopoly and (iii) the great civic enterprise and pride of late Victorian cities and towns. The result was a hopeless compromise which encouraged a firm to supply electricity to one town (but no more), and for the said town to compulsorily purchase the undertaking after twenty-one years. The Act failed, a few firms showed interest but none started work. The first British town power station at Godalming, Surrey (1881–84), was the result of purely local enterprise carried out by mutual agreement, not the terms of the Act. The *Statist* magazine (1884) thought: 'the electrical infant was strangled at birth by the . . . Act'. This judgement was rather hasty, for the 1888 Act did encourage enterprise by extending the free period to forty-two years, in which a firm might make some respectable profit.

By 1900 there were about 340 undertakings at work, most of which were municipally-owned from the outset. Both the name of the basic Act and its principal use reflected opinion as to the purpose of electricity: lighting. Now a new development added a further element to the confusion: the generation of electric power over large areas, for lighting or machinery. By 1900, technology rendered it possible to generate a high voltage current which could be sent a long distance and so supply many towns; the Parsons steam turbine being the main element in this change. The Cross Committee (1898) recognised this and recommended Parliament to pass private Acts for the proposed Power Companies, which hoped to take advantage of this development. This sensible step was thwarted by the old enemies: parochialism and the monopoly-bogey. Power Company bills stood no chance of success unless they allowed their designated area to exclude big towns (the very customers that would be attractive to a businessman) which might generate their own power. Thus a proposal (1898) for a General Power Co. supplying 210 square miles and based on Chesterfield was thrown out because Sheffield and Nottingham objected: 'A most perilous innovation, prejudicial to the privileges of the great municipalities.' Power companies were created, but at a price that reduced their effectiveness as efficient companies.

Electricity's intrinsic advantages overcame this mass of obstructions: man-made laws, established coal and gas power, localism and conservatism. When

65

40 Charles Merz, (1874–1940). Many electrical pioneers are familiar text book names: Swan, Parsons, Faraday etc.; Merz is lesser known, but equally important. When he was 24 he had electrified the City of Cork. He can also take much credit for the idea and design of the national grid and modern super-power stations—as much as anyone he 'masterminded the electric revolution'.

large-scale enterprise was given its head because of intelligence and foresight (e.g. the almost unique North-East coast network which virtually monopolised 1,600 square miles) the inherent superiority of 'Prometheus unbound' was readily apparent. It is often asked: 'Why don't They (the authorities) do something about it?' Why did the muddle go on so long? There are two reasons. First, in a democracy authority is not allowed to bulldoze schemes over all and sundry: interests have to be consulted and weighed up. Secondly, public opinion is the single great check on governments, and it took time to realise the earlier mistakes and generate support for far-reaching plans of reform. It is an old and classic political problem: individual liberty, or collective efficiency? Both terms are relative, but broadly the choice is basic and permanent.

A National Grid

One of the leading electrical engineers in the first half of the present century, Charles Merz, realised the dangers of localism and the immense technical and economic advantages of large-scale networks. He wrote: 'What is fundamentally necessary is the establishment of a national trunk mains system.' On the other hand, the politician Lloyd George sensed the real barriers to this when he said of such proposals: 'Not a matter of engineering, but of politics.' The First World War demonstrated the convenience of electric power for all to see – and particularly for working new factories in remoter parts: a factor which was to be of great importance in the future. A series of official reports (see table, p. 76) emphasised this, particularly the Parsons Committee (1917) which echoed Merz and demanded central control for such a key industry. The Electricity Supply Act (1919) was the result of all this observation, but it was another compromise. It allowed local co-operation, but did not demand it (said to be *permissive* rather than *obligatory* legislation). Although the localists may well have been content with further possibilities of obstruction, the government, electrical manufacturers and a large part of public opinion was not. The Weir Report (1925) described the muddle and crystallised public opinion, in the way of the best official investigations.

In spite of the well-known advantages of big and efficient power stations, the report noted that while twenty-eight large stations generated half Britain's electric power, there were 322 stations at the other end of the scale producing only eleven per cent. Generators of AC supplied it in many incompatible frequencies (Clydeside 25 Hz; Tyneside 40 Hz, etc.). Powerful interests opposed this patchy network, mainly the manufacturers who had to cater for this medley of systems, and who were well organised in a 'trade association' (BEAMA), so constituting a strong 'pressure group'. To take one example, a given AC electric clock could not work in both Glasgow and London.

The government thought it could act more drastically than hitherto. The Electricity Supply Act (1926) set up a Central Electricity Board which was to build a 'national gridiron', as it was at first called, of transmission lines connecting power stations; it was to set official standards, end variations and generally guide the generating industry. But the old guard was strong enough to extract some concessions from the government: the CEB could not own power stations itself, and the patchwork of distribution remained untouched. Still, progress was being made at last, and the curse of 1888 was being lifted. The last pylon of the national grid went up on 5 September 1933, really one of the significant dates of British history, although it usually goes unnoticed. Frequencies were standardized at 50 Hz, and this has been used ever since. Electric generation, already a sturdy young industry, became one of the 'growth industries' between the wars. Consumption of power grew thus:

1920	730,000 consumers and 3,773 million kWh generated
1929	2,844,000 consumers
1939	8,920,000 consumers
1970	17,800,000 consumers and 187,064 million kWh generated

In order to help electricity in its fight against established sources of power the British Electrical Development Association (BEDA) was founded in 1919 by all

"Yes! We have no soot today!" WE USE ELECTRIC FIRES.

Hackney Electricity

306, MARE STREET E.8

41 Power competition: an example of the aggressive advertising of Hackney Corporation Electricity Department (1926), one of the more lively undertakings, in this case 'knocking' raw coal, and a play on the (then) hit song *Yes, we have no bananas . . . today*.

interested parties, like BEAMA. It extolled the virtues of the new 'modern' power (**41**) in a long and lively advertising campaign. Suppliers did the same, and the affair almost had the flavour of a crusade. 'All-electric homes' were put on view in new suburbs, glittering showrooms displayed a variety of new electric gadgets (**38**) and with suitable thrift, Dumfries County Council sent a converted bus out on a propaganda mission for electric cooking (1932). Among the most vigorous competitors was Hackney Council in London, which battled on with the Gas Light and Coke Co. in a David-and-Goliath combat, quoting 'satisfied and delighted' housewives in its advertising copy. By 1934, the state watchdog for electricity, the Electricity Commissioners, said that ninety-nine per cent of the population lived in districts where there was, or soon would be, electricity supply. On the other hand, only a third of Britain's homes were actually connected; by 1944 three-quarters had been.

The difficulty of rural electrification is obvious – remote farms and villages are costly to connect, whereas town houses lie on streets under which mains run. Tests carried out in the 1930s suggested that rural electrification might pay its way if given an initial subsidy. From 3,700 miles of rural supply lines (1929) there were 30,000 miles in 1937, although this only powered 5,000 of Britain's (then) 450,000 farms. This was a modest but important start in giving farmers clean and safe power for a host of processes from cow milking to crop drying, and in that farms could have wireless sets, etc., it made rural life less isolated.

Nationalisation

The excellent work of the CEB went on apace, as can be noted from the spread of the grid:

1933	3,675 miles of 132 kV lines
1944	5,142 ,, ,, ,, ,, ,,
1970	13,433 ,, ,, ,, ,, ,,
	2,208 miles of 275 kV $\left.\right\}$ the 'supergrid' of very high voltage
	4,747 miles of 400 kV

Another state enterprise, the NSHEB (1943–see p. 15) was charged with developing hydro-electricity in the Scottish Highlands and creating some employment and prosperity in a depopulated and run-down area. The success of the CEB was one factor behind the Electricity Act (1948) which nationalised the entire industry (for £508 million) and thus, at one stroke, axed the old framework and finally ended supply confusion. The industry was vested in a new British Electricity Authority, and has since been reorganised a number of times (see table). By the Electricity Act (1957) the Central Electricity Generating Board took over generation, while twelve area boards distribute it to consumers. These boards, which date from 1948, have become a well-known part of the areas they serve; most people in Liverpool or Llandudno know of MANWEB, and most in Bristol of SWEB, although an outsider might be mystified at these esoteric local words.

Ireland and The Isles

The logic behind these changes forced similar ones elsewhere. In the Republic of Ireland there is a notable grid system, and the state-pioneered large-scale hydro-electric development. The Electricity Supply Board (1927) was formed by the state to manage the Shannon scheme, and since that time it has absorbed a variety of small undertakings (sixteen municipal, five private). The Shannon scheme has been supplemented by others: River Liffey (1937), Erne (1946) and Lee (1952), and because Ireland's hydro-electric potential is limited, the ESB has added orthodox and peat-burning stations – by 1970 nearly one-third of the Republic's electric power came from peat, and one station is fired by native

42 The Shannon scheme: power being made to obtain further power; two of the 210-ton giant dredgers digging an 8-mile channel for the Shannon hydro-electric scheme in Ireland (1926) by which Eire hoped to become independent of imported fuel. Because of the high cost of such coal, water power has a long history in Ireland, the power house at Ardnacrusha was opened in 1929 by when the scheme had cost $£5\frac{1}{2}$ million.

Irish coal at Arigna, Co. Roscommon. In Northern Ireland there is a separate system; power is generated by the Electricity Board for Northern Ireland (1931) and Belfast Corporation.

The Isle of Man and the Channel Islands have electric power systems, for instance the States (the legislature) of Guernsey took over the island's system in 1933 and now runs a completely modern one from its own power station at St Sampson's. Even remote St Kilda, sporadically occupied, and nearly the remotest British Isle, has its own electricity system, without which no modern community could remain 'civilised' (as we mean it) for very long.

Power Stations and Pylons

Power stations are probably the most vital structures in a modern economy. Curiously, they receive little attention from artists, poets, historians, journalists, etc., and are subsequently taken rather for granted. But let there be no mistake: in fifty years they have become the 'hearts' of economic life, and the grid the main 'artery' – a fact well appreciated by Germany in the Second World War, as some older stations, with their relics of camouflage remind us. There are now fewer stations in Britain than when the Weir Committee reported (1925) – 210 in

England and Wales – but their output is far greater, once more exemplifying 'more with less'.

It had long been known that a few giant stations were superior to myriads of dwarf ones, but political facts stood in the way of following engineering advice; the scientist Sylvanus Thompson (1901) wrote: 'The secret of economic working is to generate on a large scale'. The CEB encouraged such working from 1926, although where local conditions permitted it a few regional mammoths had been built, like North Tees (1917). These large stations have now become familiar: Battersea which towers over London's 'South Bank', Yoker, Glasgow, and Barton, Manchester. The location of stations has always depended on varying factors: rivers for cooling water, the proximity of coalfields and the position of the 'market' – thus Ironbridge station was built on the banks of the Severn, and the Ferrybridge stations near the Yorkshire coalfield. In recent years some experimental nuclear stations have been sited away from centres of population for safety reasons, e.g. Dounreay in the far North of Scotland (**64**).

Although called power 'stations' they were originally called power houses. Before even the ancient power houses, early generation was frequently by a mobile boiler or engine, perhaps mounted on a traction engine. Such was the case with the pioneer Holborn Viaduct scheme (1878). The first central station was at Godalming (1881) but it was short-lived. Brighton can claim to be the true first and it has the oldest record of power supply in the world (**44**) starting in 1882.

In London another early private concern was centred on the Grosvenor Gallery, New Bond Street (1883). It supplied current to a few neighbouring

43   The National Grid: in its youth (1937), some of the first 132 kV transmission lines near Nursling Hants. Such power lines freed industry from its coal-based haunts. The functional design looks well against the evening sky. 'Pylon' is the popular name for suspension towers.

premises and was so popular that it built a more permanent station (1885) and supplied its ever-growing market by a cat's cradle of overhead wires swinging over the rooftops from Regent's Park to Knightsbridge. The young engineer of the company which bought the Grosvenor Gallery scheme (London Electric Supply Corporation) was S. Z. de Ferranti, who quickly saw the advantages of big central power stations, built near rivers and easily supplied with rail- or water-borne coal – it is said he was influenced by the principle of Beckton gas-works (**25**). Current would be sent from such a station at a high voltage, over a large area. Ferranti persuaded the directors of the LESC to build such a station (Deptford, 1888) South-East of London, on the Thames.

The Deptford plan was brilliant in conception, but rather too far ahead of engineering talent, as it then was. The LESC sunk a great deal of money in the plan, but it paid no dividend until 1905. Electricity was regarded as a local lighting source, so Ferranti sold his idea as being 'capable of lighting two million lamps' – enough to illumine all London. Recurring mechanical trouble dogged the scheme, and frustrated him. The first 'peak demand' crisis of all time came in the November fog of 1891 which strained the equipment; the LESC chairman, J. S. Forbes, explained to angry shareholders and customers that 'the whole thing came to a collapse, and for four days we were without light'. Forbes was the first in a long line of harrassed power chiefs facing an irate public, and although his crisis was more acute, it has a certain modern ring to it.

Nevertheless, the 'Ferranti plan' succeeded in the long run, and is taken as standard today: big, well-situated stations serving large areas. In the meantime, the small stations which were beneficiaries of the 1882 and 1888 Acts continued to flourish. They lacked the grandeur and scale of Ferranti stations, and were often poorly designed and cramped. A visiting Italian engineer, G. Semenza (1894) described one: 'An unimposing entrance, a gloomy little back alley, and at the end the workshop of the station. A covered passage broad enough to allow a coal cart to pass traverses the workshop. On the left . . . is a coal store, and on the right . . . we find the boiler room. There is a long row of . . . boilers arranged along the passage, with a few yards between them and the wall (along which) . . . half a dozen Willans engines coupled to as many stout dynamos . . . in the engine room a grey light from the skylight, the walls are grimy . . . and there is hardly room to pass.'

After 1900 the widespread use of compact and powerful steam turbines made power stations less cluttered. Later still, they became leading examples of functional architecture, and like Victorian bridges and viaducts they showed that the age of technology can produce some superb design. The first 'futurist' power stations, like Dunston B near Newcastle (1931), were a very far cry from Semenza's squalid sheds. Modern stations like Calder Hall, the first nuclear one, built in 1956, keep the functional tradition going. The station at Bradwell, Essex, built in 1961, is set by the sea and tastefully surrounded with trees and bushes.

Within these stations another struggle has gone on, to produce more power

44 One of the first power stations (or power houses, as they were then called): the works of the Brighton Electric Co. in 1887, shortly after opening. Engines of a semi-portable type drive dynamos for arc lighting. The station worked 'daily, from dusk to 1.00 am'.

from less fuel; to create high thermal efficiency. In spite of this progress, the cost of coal rose faster than thermal efficiency. In order to discourage the power industry from importing oil as a substitute (p. 43) the government decided to press on with a nuclear power programme (1955 onwards). The nuclear reactors in the new stations were used to generate steam, which in turn drove orthodox turbines. Technical development in this field was swift, and by 1970 there were fifteen nuclear stations, producing about twelve per cent of British electricity. These stations are the result of the first programme; those of the second pro-gramme (1964) will probably be cheaper than coal-fired stations in operation. Also, the first stations, like Calder Hall are old-fashioned already, and have been eclipsed by better methods of obtaining nuclear power, as those used at Wind-scale, Cumberland; Winfrith, Dorset; and Dounreay. Experimental stations are owned by the United Kingdom Atomic Energy Authority.

Once generated, the power is transmitted to consumers – very often by means

45 *Above* Early power station: one of London's first power plants, at Victoria Embankment (1878–84) which lit arc lamps 6,000 feet either side of Waterloo bridge. Note furnace, makeshift shed and piles of coal on pavement.

46 *Below* A typical large municipal station, Birmingham Corporation's Nechells station (1926) with batteries of wooden cooling towers. This great power house is typical of major provincial stations that represented a large local investment in the great age of municipal enterprise, *c.* 1870–1940.

of the grid. It may be more economic to site a power station near a coalfield, and so send 'coal by wire' to large urban areas. Also, the grid allows power stations to help each other out in emergencies and to send surplus power (if they have it) to places where it is wanted. The grid started in 1926, and is now over 12,000 miles long. The conductor wires are suspended from pylons – 52,000 of them in England and Wales alone. The pylons are erected on land, for which the CEGB pays each affected landowner a 'wayleave'. This is no great problem; but a more serious matter has arisen over the appearance and siting of these pylons.

In the infancy of the grid, the *Electrical Review* (1929) thought 'their benefits will outweigh their inelegance'. Since those days there has been a tendency to take the benefits for granted, and to complain about their inelegance – or, at least, a vocal minority does. The matter is symbolic of a long-term problem of technological society, and is part of the great 'environment' and 'pollution' debate. Against the objectors there are two points. First, putting power lines underground would cost ten times as much as suspending them overhead, the cost involved for one hundred yards represents the value of about thirty-three new houses. Who will pay? Does the community feel it can afford such luxuries? These questions remain unanswered. Secondly, it is not universally agreed that pylons are ugly; in many places they have a pleasant functional appearance, and a striking elegance: so the debate goes on. Still, as a symbol, they remain a favourite target for those who are concerned about the 'price of progress'.

The problem is really profound, for society rarely agrees on aesthetic matters, and it is far from clear that people are willing to sacrifice hospitals, schools and houses for underground power. Instinctively, people realise the immense advantages of cheap power which lights and energises a large part of the nation and

47 Battersea power station, perhaps Britain's best known, built by the London Power Co. to the design of a leading architect, Sir Giles Gilbert Scott, 1927–33. Here (1950) the original building is being extended. Battersea, like Stonebyres (**8**) represented an important step in environmental planning: the state insisted that its exhaust should be clean, and some of its waste heat goes to serve nearby flats.

its industry. The real cost of something is what is foregone for it (*opportunity cost to economists*); so putting the matter the other way round, the pylons have released great funds for other state enterprises. In any case, sweeping pylons etched against an evening sky (**43**) can enhance the landscape, and surely they are an improvement on a blanket of lethal smog, or a treadmill! The energy they convey is vital to our life: like Henry Adams' dynamo, they are the symbols of our time.

Electricity Legislation

1870   Tramways Act: influences much of the early and poor electricity legislation
1882   Electric Lighting Act: badly framed, 21-year concessions; makes Board of Trade 'watchdog'
1888   Electric Lighting Act: 42-year concessions, rather better, though still not encouraging
1889   Electric Lighting Clauses Act: makes any amalgamation of electricity undertakings hard – compounds disadvantages of 1882 and 1888
1898   Cross Committee: recommends general power companies for big areas
1900 onwards   Various Power Co. Acts, also allows compulsory purchase of land
1906–15   London Electric Supply Acts: various unsuccessful attempts to rationalise London chaos
1909   Electric Lighting Amendment Act: compromise between company and municipal attitudes
1916   Haldane Committee: really to do with coal, but presses for few and big power stations
1916   Parsons Committee: favours central control of industry
1917   Williamson Committee: favours gradual change only
1918   Birchenough Committee: large-scale reforms suggested, but carries less weight in face of 'old guard' hostility
1919   Electricity Supply Act: watered down Williamson, permissive joint action by 'Joint Electricity Authorities', Electricity Commissioners set up to supervise industry
1922   Electricity Supply Act: fills in a few loopholes of 1919
1925   Weir Report: highlights muddle, sets the stage for:
1926   Electricity Supply Act: sets up CEB and national grid; a positive move
1936   McGowan Committee: urges big power stations, and more rapid standardisation
1942   Cooper Committee: advocates hydro-electric enterprise in Scotland, resulting in:
1943   North of Scotland Hydro-Electric Act: sets up NSHEB (see p. 69)
1948   Electricity Act: nationalised whole industry (less NSHEB) and vests it in British Electricity Authority
1955   Electricity Act: hives off South of Scotland, BEA renamed Central Electricity Authority
1956   Herbert Report: suggests changes in organisation of industry
1957   Electricity Act: breaks up CEA into CEGB and Area Boards, with an overall Electricity Council to co-ordinate.

FURTHER READING

The electricity industry, like the gas industry, has not received much attention from historians; however, various books cover important aspects of it: R. A. S. Hennessey, *The Electric Revolution* covers its origins and development 1880–1931; R. H. Parsons, *Early Days of the Power Station Industry* is exciting in parts, and always careful and accurate. H. H. Ballin's *Organisation of Electricity Supply in GB* is a complete administrative history, but is rather heavy and only goes to 1945. Percy Dunsheath, *History of Electrical Engineering* is very full and not too hard. Books on hydro-electricity are dealt with elsewhere; nuclear power is well covered in Egon Larsen's *Power From Atoms*. See also *Dictionary of National Biography*, articles on Sir Joseph Wilson Swan, Sir Charles Parsons, Charles Merz, S. Z. de Ferranti, and R. E. B. Crompton.

7 Power Applied

Whether a consumer uses this form of power or that usually depends on the relative costs and convenience of the various forms available. Such decisions face families installing central heating, or industrialists weighing up the virtues of gas and electricity; e.g. British Rail decided to abandon coal-fired steam engines for oil-fuelled diesel locomotives from 1955 onwards. If free choice alone decided these matters there would be 'consumer sovereignty', and a natural market would be the result. But this is not so: the state has to take a broader view of these matters and may deliberately slow or accelerate technical and economic change by its decrees.

Lighting

One example will show the profound changes which have flowed from technical developments. For most of man's energy-consuming era (believed to be over a third of a million years), the source of energy has been readily available primary fuels like wood, oils and fat; and coal. Coal (about two thousand years old as a fuel) is a latecomer, the others have their origins 'lost in the mists of time'. A leading historian of lighting, W. T. O'Dea, thought that: 'From fifteen or more millennia before Christ to A.D. 1782 there was practically no improvement in light at all.' The very poor had to make do for light and heat 'from the fitful gleams of a wood fire' – assuming that they had access to wood. Those who could afford it supplemented the fire with an oil-lamp, really a pot with a twisted fibre or rag wick. Others used tallow which could be made into candles, or (by dipping a rush into it) rushlight, the 'poor man's candle'. The very wealthy could afford the brighter and cleaner beeswax candles. The cost ratio of oil:tallow:beeswax was about 1:5:20, so most people were condemned to using dim and smelly oil lamps. A civilisation dependent upon such sources of light was forced to shut down every night in a way that contemporaries would find hard to bear. For instance (1791): 'Mrs Fovell sat at a small table on which in the evening stood one small candle in an iron candlestick, plying her needle by the feeble glimmer, surrounded by her maids, all busy at the same employment. . . .' External lighting was poorer. Most people avoided travelling at night, unless there was a full moon. Society had no option but to lie low until

> *Morn*
> *Waked by the circling hours with rosy hand*
> *Unbarr'd the gates of light*
> (Milton)

48 A special power station: Lot's Road, on the banks of the Thames near Chelsea (1905), erected to supply London's underground electric railways with power. It was the third largest in the world when built (and the largest in Europe) and a pioneer of new building techniques, i.e. using a steel frame rather than load-bearing walls. Also it was an early target for conservationists, who railed at the 'Chelsea Monster' that ruined a stretch of the Thames immortalised by Turner and Whistler in their paintings; others found its stark grandeur and scale very impressive. Coal was brought to it up the Thames, which also supplied water for its condensing system.

Towards the very end of the oil light era, A. Argand invented an improved lamp (1782) which used a glass chimney and multiplied the light of an oil pot ten times. At this point gas lighting arrived, although oil light remained popular in gas-less (and later electricity-less) rural areas. Oil lamp users welcomed cheap paraffin (1850) and the better distribution of oils in later years.

Gaslight was a true child of the industrial age, being coal-based and requiring a modicum of technical expertise to produce it. It made street lighting possible on the grand scale for the first time. London had 215 miles of street lights by 1823.

49 Street lighting: Christchurch Rd, Folkestone soon after electric lights were installed (1937), in this case 400 W GEC 'non-glare' lights. Note motor car, with its own modest generating plant, approaching with lights on.

Gas, the first 'artificial light' in the modern sense, suggested wide possibilities. The actor, Sir Henry Irving, for instance, varied the intensity and colour of gas-lights at the Lyceum Theatre to heighten dramatic effect; and he instituted the tradition of players being lit while the house lights were dimmed (1856), a trend which has become universal in entertainment ever since.

Gas was *de rigueur* for only a short while. It was a clear improvement on sputtering oil pots, but similarly was relatively inferior to electric light. Electric light was safer, cleaner and instantaneous. At first, however, it was very expensive. The high cost of current was compounded by the price of early bulbs: the first Swan bulbs (1882) retailed at 25 shillings (£1.25) each, although they were down to 5s (25p) the next year. Electric current cost 1s (5p) per unit, and one original customer calculated the total cost of lighting his home as £232 per year – well over £1,000 today! However, current became cheaper, and lamps also, and as a result the potential market widened, allowing mass-production of bulbs and large-scale (and therefore more efficient) generation of power. By 1930 electric lighting was commonplace, and by 1970 it was virtually universal.

Over the 1870–1970 period electric lighting has made all kinds of activities possible through the night hours. The enterprising owners of a football ground in 1878 took early action to suggest its versatility:

'The interest aroused by the application of the electric light to novel uses was strikingly apparent on Monday night in Sheffield when nearly 30,000 people gathered at Bramall-lane Grounds to witness a football match under that light. The match . . . commenced at (7.30 p.m.). The electric light was thrown from four lamps, 30 ft from the ground . . . the players being seen almost as clearly as noonday. The brilliancy of the light, however, dazzled the players, and sometimes caused strange blunders.' (*The Electrician*, 19 October, 1878.)

Gas-filled tubes for more dazzling publicity lighting came to Britain from the USA in the early 1900s, but these 'Moore tubes' were rather dangerous and usually deteriorated quickly. Neon lights, giving off a familiar red light, were far superior and made their British debut in 1913 at the West End Cinema, Coventry Street, London, and they have continued to adorn the urban night

79

scene ever since. Yellow sodium-filled street and highway lights date from 1932, and the fluorescent variety from 1947. Nowadays 'night life' is taken for granted, but for many centuries it was the privilege of the opulent few who could afford batteries of candles, so the changes described above are, socially speaking, one of power's most far-reaching achievements.

Energy

The other major use for power is to supply energy, for industrial and domestic use. The various types of energy available have already been described, and there remain some other factors affecting their relative attractions which must be considered. One is the problem of storing energy. Primitive societies did not always find this so difficult as more recent and sophisticated ones. They could go and gather some more firewood from the forests, a permanent store – or they

50 Gustave Doré's *Scripture Reading in a Night Shelter* (1872) showing the dim and localised light of 'fish-tail' gas jets employed before the gas mantle came into use; they 'lit the darkness' rather than 'made light'.

51 Electrically powered industry: Arcadia House, the Egyptian-styled works of Messrs Carreras, cigarette makers (1930): inside over 400 electric motors were powered by the local St Pancras Electricity Works, an electric tram of the LCC (powered from Greenwich see **53**) passes by. A good example of the 'electric age' arriving in the South.

could busy themselves about the unpleasant task of finding animal dung. Industrial society has tended to 'mortgage its fate' by developing power sources that are often harder to store. Coal and oil can be stockpiled, but it is not economic to build stocks beyond a given level; too much capital is tied up and idling, if so. Gas is easier to store than electricity, and gasholders were an early and convenient way of hedging against daily peak demand. Yet even these could not hold more than a few days' supply at most. Recently proposals have been put forward to hold gas in certain geological strata, and in any case natural gas exists in vast amounts, stored by nature. Gas, therefore does not present great storage problems.

But electricity, the principal power source, does. Chapter 5 noted the 'victory' of AC, by 1910. Early DC systems could store power, by using batteries rather after the manner of gasholders to ease peak demand. Alternating current cannot be stored, and so the electricity supply industry always requires rather more plant than it needs in order to be safe in case demand rises sharply. Power stations are very costly, so this is a major economic problem, and because so many people can be adversely affected by a power failure or cut, it is a political matter as well. In this way, the results of the old AC–DC battle live with us still.

Another problem is transferring energy. Early steam engines were built actually in a mine or factory. They moved pumps, or miles of belts-and-pulleys in order to do their work. However, the steam engine, even when very compact and powerful is difficult to harness *mechanically* to the varied needs of industry. A superior way of sending out its energy is by pneumatic, hydraulic or electrical means. Coal mines, which could not have boilers and steam engines in the

81

53 The Greenwich dinosaurs: some of the gigantic slow-speed alternators that powered the 68-mile LCC tramway network (1906). They were virtually obsolete when built, and were replaced by turbines. Each set generated 3,500 kw.

52 *Opposite* Arteries of power: a tracked vehicle scaling Dunslair Heights, Peebles, taking repair and inspection teams on duty. In this case 'power to maintain power' and difficult though it is, easier still than the nightmare of maintaining the underground mains advocated by the 'anti-pylon lobby'.

54 Victorian engineering, at its most magnificent. The latter-day beam engine (built by James Watt & Co.) enshrined in Egyptian columns, with moulding, winged monsters and roseate gothic windows. This astonishing blend of Victorian craftsmanship and engineering was in fact the Birmingham waterworks at Whitacre. Note the beam *under* the engine (the first ones had been *over*) and the impeccable maintenance. These engines were built 1881–3 towards the end of the steam age and a century after Watt's improvements to the classic steam pump had ushered in the age of steam-mechanical power. Birmingham's superb machinery is in a way a temple to the early technological revolution, when the steam engine 'served to define an age' (Henri Bergson).

dangerous workings below ground were among the first to avail themselves of this flexible long-distance power. The first known example of this was at Govan Colliery, near Glasgow (1849), where compressed air was used to work a pump and a hauling engine. Modern pneumatic drills date from about 1870; they were first employed in a well-publicised way when they were used on the Alpine tunnel excavation (1872–1873). Hydraulic transmission of energy (by high-pressure water or other liquid) was known before the industrial revolution, but its first dramatic application was in Bramah's hydraulic press 1795. Joseph Bramah (1748–1814) was a hydraulic engineer of singular genius; his other and rather more famous inventions being the standard modern lavatory, and the beer-pull in public houses! Another leading hydraulic power engineer was Lord Armstrong, who made the first hydraulic crane (1846), used at Newcastle Upon Tyne Quay. For a short while (*c.* 1850–1900) hydraulic power was the main way of transmitting heavy energy, to work cranes, lifts, presses, etc., but although still occasionally employed, it was rapidly overtaken by electric power.

If power is available over really large areas, there is no universal need for towns and industries to huddle around primary fuel sources. Even in Victorian times coal was widely available by rail or sea routes, and large coal yards could be found near most stations as the local 'power reserve'. Coal was retailed by coal merchants (**13**), many of whom were household names, for example Messrs Charringtons, or Cory. However, there was an appreciable difference in price between coal at the pithead and in (say) the heart of Suffolk; hence, the need for many industries that used a lot of coal to be near coalfields.

Electric power, on the other hand, is nationally available at fairly uniform prices. The fact that it was widely available has had great effect on industrial location, especially since 1919. Industries which needed to be near big markets, like Greater London, could do so. Factories were erected in places which had hitherto been relatively free of industrialism: Luton, Slough, Oxford, etc. Electricity, and especially the first grid (1926–1933), was the single major factor in shifting the economic centre of Britain 'South of the Trent'. Lord Macaulay in 1830 foresaw all this with strange prescience: 'Sussex and Huntingdonshire will be wealthier than the wealthiest parts of the West Riding of Yorkshire . . . machines constructed on principles yet undiscovered will be in every home' – in just a year Faraday was to discover the principles. Later in the nineteenth century, the Rev. W. Tuckwell in *New Utopia, or England in 1985*, published in 1885, forecast: 'electricity has superseded the diminishing coalfields and become the sole vehicle of light, heat, motion, force . . .'. Tuckwell did not guess at oil and natural gas, which have marred his accuracy, but broadly speaking he was on the right lines. These prophets sensed that changes in power production were to alter the whole base and appearance of society.

Power and the State

Because of the quite fundamental importance of power, the state has assumed a key position in ensuring that there is enough power, at the right price and time, to answer the needs of society. 'Our civilisation is based on power' was the prosaic but unchallengeable assertion of the government paper *Programme For Nuclear Power* (1955). At first, state intervention was very modest (1780–1920), when it restricted its activities to granting local monopolies and establishing minimum safety standards. As in so many matters, the First World War came as an abrupt break in this tradition. The state assumed temporary control of the coal industry (1916–1921), and found itself repeatedly helping or intervening in it ever afterwards. The need for more electric power, and the parochial organisation of its supply, sprung a number of key investigations by official committees, and two Acts (1919, 1926), the latter of which showed a major change of attitude: the state was now taking steps to reshape the whole industry. After the Second World War the state has not waited on events, but rather given a major lead in planning the whole power pattern for the economy.

55 Gas engines: between the steam age, and the electricity-and-diesel one of today, the gas engine enjoyed a 'brief vogue'. Such machines used coal gas, or various industrial gases like this one here (Britain's largest at the time) a 1909 German built 2,400 hp set using coke-oven gas at Bargoed, South Wales, and in turn powering the 170 electric motors of the Powell Duffryn Steam Co., big coal operators thereabouts. Like the old horsegin, it is 'power for power' again (**9**).

56 Portable power: energy is often hard to store, being bulky and dirty (like coal) or inconvenient (like electric batteries); gas has some advantages here, especially for camping. Here is the Calor Gas sea terminal at Plymouth, smaller containers take the pressurised gas to customers.

57 and **58** Power/weight technology: much effort and expense has gone into producing more with less in power matters. **57** *Above* shows an LNWR Anglo-Scottish express train, of about 400 tons weight (*circa* 1920 hauled by a 78-ton engine burning about 50 lbs of coal per mile, and occasionally touching 1,200 hp and 80 mph; a special fireman fuelled the machine. **58** *Below* shows the Blackburn *Iris* flying-boat, built within a dozen years of 57, weighing but 10 tons, powered by three 675 hp engines and flying at 115 mph consistently—with one pilot. It carried fewer passengers than the train, but the general concept of 'more with less' is clear.

59 Fire power: another aspect of man's extension—here as a killer of other men; arms salesmen have just demonstrated to foreign customers (Chinese mandarins in this case) the devastating effects of a machine gun, which has sliced down a tree. Control and production of 'military hardware' like this gives its owners great political power. This gun was a Maxim, *c.* 1895.

60 *Opposite* The Politics of Power: The State has often had to concern itself with fuel prices and supplies, so basic to social and economic life. In many cases gas companies had statutory limits on profits, here is evidence of the perennial public outcry about high fuel costs (1900) with radical and Labour criticism to the fore; the very elements which demanded, and later got, nationalisation of most power industries in an effort to control them.

IMPORTANT TO GAS CONSUMERS.

A Public Meeting,

TO PROTEST AGAINST

The Exorbitant Price of Gas,

Will be held in the Hall of the

PADDINGTON RADICAL CLUB,

PADDINGTON GREEN, W.,

On Tuesday, December 4th, 1900.

The Chair will be taken at 8.30 p.m. by

C. B. GROSSMITH, ESQ.

(President of the Paddington Radical Club), supported by
the following Gentlemen :—

B. S. STRAUS, ESQ., L.C.C.

JESSIE ARGYLE, ESQ.   JOHN EARLEY, ESQ.

E. GARRITY, ESQ.

(Assist. Sec. of the Amalgamated Society of Railway Servants.)

J. EDDS, ESQ.   EMANUEL HOPE, ESQ.

JAMES ROWLANDS, ESQ.

(President of the Gas Consumers' Protection League.)

Clubs' and Societies' Branch of the Gas Consumers' Protection
League. Headquarters: Mildmay Radical Club.

Secretary, EDWARD J. EDWARDS.

W. F. MORGAN, Printer, Rosebery Printing Works, 86, Rosebery Avenue, E.C.

61 and **62** The price of progress: an early and humorous observation on the now-familiar theme. Richard Dighton's cartoons (*circa* 1825) imply that there is little to choose between the mess of oil, and the explosive dangers of coal gas. In spite of exaggeration he has a point—each new form of power is more efficient, but carries greater potential dangers. Experience and technical research have shown us how to control new sources.

Specifically, the government set up a Ministry of Fuel and Power (1939, renewed 1945 and merged into the Ministry of Technology 1969). This Ministry was held responsible for: 'securing effective and co-ordinated development . . . of fuel and power in Great Britain, . . . promoting economy and efficiency in supply, distribution, use and consumption . . .'. Previously such matters had been dealt with in a limited way by the Board of Trade or the Ministry of Transport, but not in accordance with any strong strategy. Next, the government nationalised coal in 1946, electricity in 1948 and gas in 1949 – oil still remains a private industry. Finally, a number of reports and policy statements, occasionally embodied in a statute, have guided the power industries on their way.

A great deal of initiative and planning is left to the industries which continue to compete with each other. This is no paradox: by leaving sufficient 'natural market' the government can see the true tendencies at work; it intervenes to humanise or rationalise the resulting conditions. For example, it has protected the coal industry for over twenty years, by forcing the electricity industry to use coal-fired power stations when it preferred oil-fired ones, and by putting a tax on oil. The electricity producers did not take kindly to this intervention, and observed: 'Major plant investment decisions . . . must be aimed at securing the cheapest generating costs' (CEGB Report, 1969). The state has wider responsibilities than power station planners and managers, however. It has to bear in mind such factors as the cost of oil imports, regional unemployment in coalfields, loss of business to coal-carriers like British Rail, loss of employment by mining engineers, etc. However, it remains essential that electricity men speak out, to remind governments and public opinion of the other consideration: cheap and plentiful power.

The main postwar reports and statutes have been:

1945   Ministry of Fuel and Power Act
1946   Coal Industry Nationalisation Act (takes effect 1/1/47)
1946   Atomic Energy Act
1947   Electricity Act (effective 1948)
1948   Gas Act (effective 1949)
1950   Plan For Coal (NCB) advocates greater mechanisation in view of big expected demand
1952   Ridley Committee on fuel requirements, thought 1950 plan too modest
1954   United Kingdom Atomic Energy Authority charged with developing nuclear power
1955   *Programme For Nuclear Power* outlines development and shows that government backs this energy which Ridley Committee gave 'less attention than peat'
1956   Clean Air Act attacks smoke pollution, therefore hits open coal grates
1956   Herbert Report advocates oil and nuclear primary fuels for electricity, various financial ideas
1956   *Investing in Coal* NCB revises 1950 plan and suggests more opencast mining to lower costs
1957   Capital Investment report, compares fuel costs
1959   *Revised Plan for Coal*, recognises falling demand and tough competition

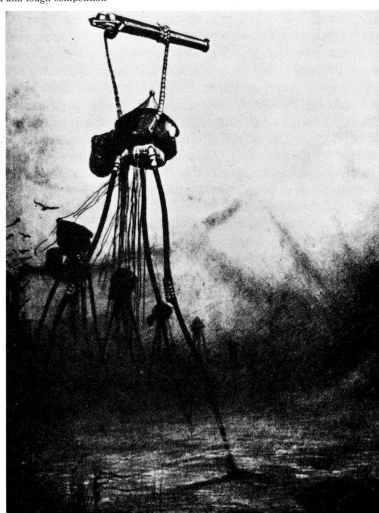

63 'Cyborgs' (cybernetic organisms)—an impression by Alvim-Correa of the Martian fighting machines described by H. G. Wells in his scientific romance *The War of the Worlds* (1898). These machines were used by Martian invaders to terrorise Southern England—'walking machines of glittering metal' worked by creatures within, and so amplifying or extending them. Wells' prophetic machines were long ahead of their time, and are now being considered for terrestrial and space use; a dramatic and obvious way in which power can extend man.

64 Nuclear power: the nuclear station at Dounreay, Caithness (1963) its 150 MW sets are driven by normal steam turbines, but the steam is generated by the heat from nuclear fission; a totally science-based process that frees electricity generation from the old fossil fuels.

1959–60   Ministry of Power forces CEGB to use more coal, although oil getting cheaper
1963   Finance Act (the enacted 'budget') put 2d per gallon duty on oil to make it less of a threat to coal
1964   Second Nuclear Programme expands this energy beyond 1955 plan
1965   Energy Advisory Council set up to advise government on long-term plans
1965   *White Paper on Fuel Policy*, recognises Great Britain now a 'four fuel' economy, and observes trends at work and what should be done
1967   *White Paper on Fuel Policy*, reviews 1965 in light of rapid development of nuclear power and natural gas; opines sharp run-down of coal industry.

Many of these reports will be seen to modify or cancel previous ones, and many are about the coal problem. Reviews in quick succession do not necessarily imply incompetence: they reflect the great speed of technological development, and the difficulty of making accurate forecasts.

Beyond the purely British scene one can see all these problems on a global scale. There is increasing international inter-dependence in matters of fuel and power, for example Canada and the USA sharing Niagara's hydro-electric potential; the sales of electricity between France and England (they are connected by an undersea power cable); the discussion of long-term mutual problems and changes at World Power Conferences (1924 onwards), and the existence of various international committees on the subject. The need for power is common and basic, and so represents a promising field for international co-operation on a large scale.

The gas and electricity grids are the 'bones' or 'lifelines' of our civilisation. They give life and energy to our industry-based societies. Without this flow of power the economy, and the body-politic dependent on it, would rapidly dissolve and collapse. Our civilisation, and any hope it has to offer, depends on a wide variety of artefacts that transport, communicate, build and so on. Power is the life source for all these phenomena, without it they are nothing, and we would rapidly degenerate into barbarism, or worse.

FURTHER READING

Mechanical history is to be found in A. F. Burstall, *History of Mechanical Engineering*, J. G. Crowther, *Discoveries and Inventions of the Twentieth Century*. For addicts there is a 5-volume *History of Technology* by Singer, Holmyard, Hall and Williams. The stationary steam engine has been well studied: see L. T. C. Rolt, *Thomas Newcomen*, R. J. Law, *The Steam Engine* and H. W. Dickinson, *A Short History of the Steam Engine*.

Some, though not all, people may have access to some of Britain's excellent technological and science museums, with their rich collections of early machines and power apparatus. See: *Science Museum* (South Kensington, London); *Museum of Science and Industry* (one at Birmingham, another at Newcastle Upon Tyne) and the *Royal Scottish Museum* at Edinburgh.

For those interested in exploring the remains of past sources and uses of power, see Kenneth Hudson *Industrial Archaeology*.

Index

The numerals in **bold** type refer to figure numbers of the illustrations.

Abadan crisis (1950), 41
Aberfan disaster, 5
Adams, Henry, (qu.), 63, also 76
Accidents, 5, 27
'All-Electric' homes, 68
Anthracite, 22
Argand, A., 78
Arkwright, Richard, 14
Armstrong, Lord, 15, 84

Beckton gasworks, 56, 72; **25, 26**
Bevercotes, 31
Big Ben, **10**
Bituminous coal, 22
Brámah, Joseph, 84
Brighton, 59, 60, 71; **44**
Bristol, 23, 24, 32

Cannel coal, 22, 24, 51
Carboniferous era, **12**
Central Electricity Board, 67
Central Heating, 57, 77
Churchill, Sir Winston, 40
Clean Air Act, 91; **15**
Clegg, Samuel, 46
Clockwork, 19; **10**
Coal, Chapter 3
  Exchanges, 22
  Fields, 22
  Legislation, 34
  Miners, 31 ff.
  Output statistics, 26, 29
  Types, 22
Coal Utilisation Council, 29
Coke, 22, 47–8
Consumers
  of electricity, 67
  of gas, 56
Cornwall, 7, 13, 26
Cossham, Handel, 23

Daventry, **35, 36**
Davidson, Robert, 59
Denison, Sir E. Beckett, QC, *see* Grimthorpe

Deptford power station, 72; **39**
Disraeli, Benjamin, *Sybil* (qu.), 33
Domesday Survey, 13
Dounreay nuclear power station, 71; **64**
Drake, E. L., 39
Dudley Port, *see* Tipton

East Indies, 39; **19**
Edinburgh, **15**
Edward I, 24
Electricity, Chapter 6
  Appliances, **38**
  Commissioners, 68
  Consumers, 67
  Engineering, 62–3; **39**
  Frequency and voltage, 64–5 and 67
  Legislation, 65, 67, 76
  Lighting, 58–9; **33, 37, 49**
  Publicity, 67–8; **41**
  Supply, 64 ff.
  Technology, 58–63
  Telecommunications, 60; **34–36**
Electricity Supply Board (Ireland), 69
Environment, 5, 7, 8; **47–48**
Evelyn, John, 24
Exports and Imports, 28–9, 44
External diseconomies, 24

Falls of Clyde, 15; **8**
Faraday, Michael, 58, 85
Fawley refinery, **22**
Ferranti, S. Z. de, 64, 72; **39**
Forbes, J. S., 72
Fossil fuels, Chapters 3 and 4; 8, 9
Fuel crisis (1947), 30–31
Fuller, Buckminster, 7

Gas, Chapter 5
  Appliances, 52, 56, 57
  Companies, 54–6
  Cooking, 51
  Engines, **55**
  Holders, 48; **25, 32**
  Legislation, 56

Gas, Chapter 5 _cont._
  Meters, 52
  Portable, 48, 53; **56**
  Technology, 45 ff.
  Statistics, 56–7
  Types, 45, 53
  Works, 48–9; **25, 26, 32**
Gas Light and Coke Co., 47–8, 55–6, 68;
    25–26
Godalming, 65, 71
Grids, 93
  electricity, 67, 73, 75, 85; **43, 52**
  gas, 47–9, 53–6
  oil, 43
Grimthorpe, Lord, **10**
Guernsey, 70

Hackney, 68; **41**
Halifax, **1**
Heathfield, 53–4
Horses, **2, 9**
Hydro-electricity, 15, 17, 29; **8, 42**

Industrial Revolution, 6, 7, 14, 25, 84
Ireland, 15, 17, 22, 34, 69–70; **42**
Iron Duke, HMS, **21**

Jevons, Stanley, 28

Kent coalfield, 23; **14**

Labour-intensive industry, 28
Law of Diminishing Returns, 29
Leland, John, 24
Lenin, V. I., 5
Lighting, 77 ff.
Lignite, 22–3
Lloyd George, David, (qu.), 65
Lurgi process, 48

Macaulay, Lord (qu.), 85
Mains, _see_ Grids
Man, Fall of, 5
  as 'engine', 6
Manchester, 46, 54
Merz, Charles, 66–7; **40**
Mining technology, 26 ff.
Muggeridge, Malcolm, (qu.), 5
Murdoch, William, 45, 47

Nationalisation, 90
  coal, 31
  electricity, 69
  gas, 55; **60**
Natural gas, 53 ff., 85; **31**
Neon lighting, 79

Newcastle-upon-Tyne, 84; **17, 33**
Newcomen, Thomas, 26
North of Scotland Hydro-Electric Board, 15,
    17, 69

O'Dea, W. T. (qu.), 77
Oil, Chapter 4
  Companies, 40
  Early days, 36; **18**
  Refineries, 41; **18, 19, 22**
Opportunity costs, 76
Orwell, George, _The Road to Wigan Pier_ (qu.), 33
Oxfordshire, coal reserves in, **14**

Paraffin, 38–9, 78
Parsons turbine, 7, 65
Patent fuel, 28; **16**
Peat, _see_ Turf
Petroleum Board, 43–4
Pipelines, 43
'Pool' petrol, 44
Power (political, military), 5, 8; **59**
Power Companies, 65
'Power for power', 28, 29; **3, 9, 23, 27, 52, 55**
Power stations, 70 ff.; **8, 44–48, 53**
Power/weight ratio, **57–58**
Primary fuel, 6
Productivity, 29, 31
'Pylons', 70, 75–6; **43**

Railways, 28, 29, 48, 72, 77, 84; **57**
Reid Report, 31
Rochdale, **32**
Royalties, 22
Rural electrification, 69

St Kilda, 70
Sailing ships, 10; **3**
Sea coal, 24, 56; **25**
Secondary fuel, 6
Semenza, G., 72
Severn barrage, 15; **6**
Shale oil, 38, 41; **18**
Shannon, River, 17, 69; **42**
Solar power, Chapter 2
Soyer, Charles, 51
State and power, Chapter 7, also 11, 15, 17, 24,
    27, 30, 33, 34, 40, 43, 47, 56, 58
Steam engines, 14, 21, 26; **53, 54, 57**
Storage of power, 48, 80–81; **10**
Suburbs, 60
Sun, _see_ Solar Power
Swan, Sir Joseph Wilson, 58; **33**

Tallow, 36, 77
Taxes, 24, 43

Telecommunications, 60; **34–36**
Thompson, Sylvanus (qu.), 71
Thwaite, B. H., 5, 53; **15, 55**
Tide mills and power, 15; **6**
Tipton, 53; **27, 28, 29**
Trade Unionism, 32
Tuckwell, Rev. W. (qu.), 85
Tunbridge Wells Gas Co., 55–6
Turf, 21, 34–5

United Kingdom Atomic Energy Authority, 73

Vacuum cleaners, **38**

Water power, 13, 14; **5, 6**; *see also*
    Hydro-electricity
Watt, James, 26, 45, 47; **54**
Weir Report (1925), 67, 70
Wells, H. G., 32; **63**
Westminster Palace Clock, **10**
Windmills, 10, 11, 12; **4**
Wind power, Chapter 2
Wood fuel, 7, 25

Yenangyuang, 38; **20**
Young, James, 36, 38